Screams and Silences

SCREAMS
AND
SILENCES
EDITED BY LEONE ROSS

fp FINCHAM PRESS

First published 2015
Published by Fincham Press
        University of Roehampton
        Department of English and Creative Writing
        80 Roehampton Lane
        London SW15 5PH, UK

Design by Rudolf Ammann
Typeset in Calluna and Calluna Sans
Printed and bound by printondemand-worldwide.com
Printed in England

British Library Cataloguing in Publication Data
A catalogue record for this book is available from
the British Library.

ISBN 978-0-9928581-2-4

1. Creative writing; 2. University press; 3. Fiction; 4. Poetry

CONTENTS

FOREWORD

With *Screams and Silences*, Fincham Press is delighted to publish a second anthology of student work.

The Press is part of a new wave of innovation in publishing taking place in British universities, with the potential to add innovation in *process* to experiments in content. The anthologies offer a new way to serve our students, past and present; just as their contribution enriches Fincham Press and its host, the Department of English and Creative Writing at the University of Roehampton.

From 2016, we plan a modest expansion of the publisher's list to include educational material, essay collections and works for a general audience. The focus, overall, is on work that reflects a belief in the value of English Literature and Creative Writing as subjects for teaching and research.

This year the editorial board enjoys the expertise of a new member, Dustin Frazier Wood, and the continued insights of designer Rudolf Ammann. A big thanks is given to all those who helped make this second anthology possible, with a special nod to the student editorial team, for its careful work in producing a long list from the competition entries; and to colleagues Jeff Hilson and Peter Jaeger, who judged the poetry entries. As always, the project owes a huge debt to the support of our head of department, Laura Peters.

Dustin Frazier Wood
Susan L Greenberg
Leone Ross

INTRODUCTION
Leone Ross

The work published here started life as entries for an annual Creative Writing Day competition, open to students in the Department of English and Creative Writing, at the University of Roehampton. Submissions can be in any of the forms taught within our department – screenwriting, narrative nonfiction, formally innovative poetry, writing for performance and fiction. Winners are offered the chance to give a public reading of their work at the *soirée*, an audience of current and former students, faculty, jobbing writers and industry guests.

The first job for a writing competition judge is to identify good work. Writing with the capacity to move the reader. Language that inspires Samuel Taylor Coleridge's 'willing suspension of disbelief'. Form or structure that creates an interesting receptacle for ideas. When things are going well, an entry can make you put down the work and smile, or wince at the hard truth of it all.

The next stage of the editorial process involves settling down with that 'good work' and seeing what you have in front of you, by way of a *collection*. Is it *more* than 24 pieces of good writing? Is it a thing with its own life; a work of art that hangs together? A book's identity can be harder to define when the work is a mix of forms, with no set theme. But this time, sitting at the soirée, listening to Marita Algroy read from her poetic sequence *Screams & Silences* – an ode, if there ever was one, to the work of Edvard Munch – the meaning of the book became clear.

Afterwards, I sifted through the entries to see if this

hunch was right. It was. From *Bring Your Own Sun*, Silje Heum's dispassionate take on the hidden narratives of London immigrant life, to the painful silence of Nika Cobbett's little girl in *One of Those*; and from the rebel heroine in Fionnuala Bland's witch trial story *Fire* to the female ex-military 'biobot' from Jo Schinas' science fiction novel *Headware*, this is a collection concerned with the silence of secrets, and what happens when they are screamed out loud.

More than anything, the work of this year's winners is a testimony to the lives of children. In most cases that testimony is moving, because it is so sad. In *Running Away*, Elliot Codling's protagonist feels a puzzling compulsion with no real answer. Emily Parson's *Pinewood* is a tale of a boy bringing up his sister in the shadow of alcoholism. Sean Wai Keung's trio of poems, particularly *Obscene Art*, is on parental relationships gone wrong; in Cleo Wreford's horror tale, *Lunam*, yet another alcoholic parent gets his sticky comeuppance. Katherine Gutierrez's magic realist *Angel Mountain* reminds of us of the complicated effects of parental abandonment. Victoria Stevens' *Star Theory* recounts the tenderness of a first kiss between two stargazing boys; Nanou Blair Gould's *Just Games* is a dark tale of middle class humour and bullying counter-culture.

And so this book belongs to young people; their excruciating secrets, coping strategies and heroism. It is a reminder that our childhoods, whether dark or bright, are hidden from the rest of the world; and a reminder of how identities can be solidified in a single night, or summer. Childhood experiences stay with us for such a long time, in ways that may not be apparent until we read writing like this. We will not be silent, our writers seem to say – we will speak for those who won't speak, or cannot.

The collection contains no nonfiction this year, but the writing still feels like an act of witness. This is hardly surprising. According to statistics compiled by the National Society for the Prevention of Cruelty to Children (NSPCC), one in every twenty British children is sexually abused; one in every fourteen has been physically abused; one in every five has been exposed to domestic abuse and in a single year (2013) 45,000 children talked to Childline about bullying. As we are often reminded, these numbers reflect the few children who do not remain in silence.

Parents are not mere ciphers or monsters in this book – they are humanised, not least in a trio of tales about families. Victoria Simpkins' stage play, *Birthday*, provides a glimpse into the life of a mother at the end of her marriage. Francoise Macaly's *Mother's Day* is a tough and tender tale about domestic abuse that also addresses immigrant experience. Karoline Vembre's haunting *Achromatic* follows the struggles of a father trying to save his children from suicide.

The screams and silences are not all about families or childhood. Love, longing and sex are also here, and sardonic word play. The poetry provides a kind of respite – a thematic and structural alternative that declares itself throughout. Charlotte Taverner's *A Trap For A Mole* is a gorgeous romp through a fairground – and, says the writer, some of the best fun she's ever had. Audrey Jean's *721st day of falling* evokes stars falling through the sky. Algroy's titular *Screams & Silences* is deliberately positioned in the middle of the book, for its sensuality, vivid colour and shifting moods. Erica Gillingham's nod to American poet Kim Addonizio is a poem that embodies the urgency of desire and continues our tradition of delicious titles (as in last year's *My Slut's Lofty With Solid Plump Eggs* by Hedda Estensen).

Gillingham sits well alongside Maja Hagen Torjussen's madly dysfunctional love in her short story, *Long Legs*, and with Jamie Hubner's numbed protagonist, still in love with maybe-Jayne in the silly and funny *Happy Hour*. Karoline Vembre's second piece, the poem *Movement*, is so stuffed full of ideas that one has to pause at nearly every line in delighted contemplation: 'To be a millimetre. A sigh in a multitude. A brick. A beginning. A break down, my dear.' Haley

Jenkins' huffy retired academic brings up the rear in *Ugly*, a darkly comic take on materialism and beauty.

It was the Austrian writer and musician Alfred Brendel who pointed out that the words 'listen' and 'silent' use exactly the same letters. We hope you will listen carefully to the screams in the silence, in this collection, and the silence in the screams.

ONE OF THOSE

Nika Cobbett

This is my Dad with the big, painful hands and the pleading voice.

Every school holiday, me and him have our special trip together; never abroad, just away. This year we went to Blackpool. Mum tried to convince me it would be fun, only she never actually said fun, she said Blackpool had history. All I could think of was how I'd be adding to its bloodier side if they weren't careful. I'm eleven; I'm not a stupid kid. I know this isn't normal.

In the car with Dad on the way to Blackpool I forgot I was supposed to be older now. Smarter. I sank right back into being that seven year-old, the first time in Newquay at a grotty B&B, two miles inland. No one goes two miles inland in Newquay, it's a sad wasteland. The place we stayed looked like it was once white but then the shadows started sticking in the corners. A creaking sign said 'Ne-quay's F-nest'. When we went up to the counter, Dad said he wanted a double room, the old lady looked down at me but I couldn't tell what she was thinking, she asked if he wanted a cot or something in the room for me and he said no, that's alright, love.

Driving into Blackpool it's still the same: eleven years old, still sharing the bed. Another old lady looking over the desk at me and I can tell she thinks it's weird, but I'm older now so she doesn't say anything.

You can handle yourself when you're older, and I almost do. I nearly tell her, nearly speak up, nearly say yes, I want a separate bed, a separate room! But I don't and so five minutes later me and Dad are walking up yet another set of dirty stairs, threadbare red carpet that hasn't been changed or cleaned since the 60's and sand in all the corners. This one is close to the seafront, but that doesn't mean much. It's raining and there's no one outside selling candyfloss or cone bags of marshmallows, only a couple of determined hen parties with cheap plastic shot glass necklaces and dangling penis earrings.

Up in the room, I dump my stuff and sit down on a chair in front of the kettle and mirror. Can some people not stand and make a cup of tea? I read the leaflets on fun things to do in Blackpool, seven casinos, two swimming pools (by the sea?) a handful of fish and chip shops (all Blackpool's Best), nightclubs with men dressed as women and of course, the pleasure beach. That's fun, something I can get behind. I reckon it'd probably take a while to see it all as well, two days? Dad had finished unpacking. I watch his reflection, walking up behind me in the mirror, slow.

'Hey, Dad.' I thrust the leaflet behind me so he has to stop and read it.

'Pleasure beach, eh?' He throws the words around, rolling them in his mouth. 'Pleasure beach, we can do that.' He just wants the pictures. Mum always demands pictures.

My thin jumper soaks through in the twenty-minute walk up the sea front, and when we get there, they have a big sign with the prices on. Dad hands over a pile of coins and a couple of notes, does that weird sorry scrunchy face and the man behind the counter just stares for a second, before starting to count. He gives us little tokens for the rides and games.

We get in and when Dad starts fiddling around with the lockers, that's my cue to run. I spend the day shivering and spinning my way round Blackpool's graveyard. The fastest and highest rollercoasters are shut down, 'cause of bad weather. But I'm so small I don't meet the height restrictions anyway. The ones I can get on are enough to pull me out of myself for a little while. When I've used all my tokens, I wander round, watching the families that have planned a day out and hell or high water isn't going to stop them: the mum dragging a toddler, telling him the washed out chip-munk statue with patches of green moss covering his face was fun and bright. The kid just kind of stares at her. One old couple are celebrating their anniversary: fifty years ago they'd been here and got engaged and now they're walking round trying hard not to be disappointed, but you can see their hearts hanging round each other's necks.

Hours later, I hear the closing signal. I don't know which way is out. A woman walks up to me. All blonde hair and smiles and alien values and in the broadest Geordie ac-cent I've ever heard she comes out with, 'You lost, hon? Want me to take you to the Help Centre?'

All I can do is stare at this artificial sun, with all her flowery accessories and brood in tow. I stare until she gets uncomfortable. Maybe I look deaf, smell stupid. She stam-mers a bit, looking at her squashed boyfriend/husband then back to me.

'I'll just go get help then, shall I?' She scurries off, look-ing for someone and I run in the opposite direction.

Dad's waiting at the entrance for me, eating a bag of chips and staring at the girl closing up the novelty shop down the road. A salty, displaced chip hangs in Purgatory; he seems immobilised by her sweeping skills. The girl is barely older than me. I walk up behind him and shout, 'Race you back!' Like it's fun, like he'll appreciate the fun. I run all the way down the strip with him behind me, yelling 'stop' and 'you'll be sorry'. All the old staples.

I pretend I'm flying down the long alleyway near my house, being chased by my younger brother, it's sunny and I have to swat the flimsy branches out of my face and look back, make sure I'm not going too fast, that he hasn't fallen over. I pretend my brother is swinging his arms like pro-pellers to go faster, laughing long and loud into the violet day. He tumbles over me, knocking me to the ground and I can almost smell the baby milk that still clings to him even three years after he stopped nursing.

The pavement meets my head and I'm only half aware of Dad on top of me. Blackpool becomes this place of spinning lights that I'd been promised, and I feel like one of those hen party women stumbling on the pavement, into the road and being yanked back again.

I wake up in bed at the B&B. It takes me a lap round the room, holding on to the walls to figure out which one this is. Cornwall? Gretna Green? No, this is Blackpool. I can see the pier from my window, the one with the swing that goes over the water, with all the lights twined up its ropes. I remember falling down, hitting the pavement hard. It's dark now, and I don't know where Dad is. My head expands, sending a shockwave down to my toes. There's a swollen lump on my skull, I pull my hand away quickly. I kind of remember dead-locking the door and falling back into bed.

The next day I'm sitting across the table from Dad, down in the breakfast room; him not speaking and me not eating. I'm hungry, definitely hungry, but the grease is stuck like cling film to everything: the eggs, sausages, hash browns, even the bowl of fruit. The purple egg on my head from yesterday pulses, the room turning into a rolling, sad circus. Dad breaks his silence to tell me we're going to the beach. Through the window, I see fat grey clouds fighting each other in the sky, but no rain. He tells me to go get my swimming costume on. My head hurts too much to argue.

'And if you lock me out of the room tonight, nowhere will be safe ever again.' His spit lands on top of a pool of grease on my plate. 'I do this for you,' he says, like it's an afterthought.

I just nod.

The sea is dirty, rubbish rolling in and out on wave tips. It looks angry and forgotten and I'm supposed to strip down and get in. Dad's looking at me with his, 'Don't make me pull those clothes off you myself,' look. I hadn't put my swimming costume on; I really can't go out in that water, hadn't expected him to make me. It's carnivorous, a great dirty reptile flowing round us. When I tell Dad that, he laughs, pulls on the camera round his neck and looks out to the horizon, waiting. I take off my trainers, socks and jeans and put them in my yellow beach bag, ashamed of its happy colour and my exposed underwear. I look at Dad, who's still staring out at the horizon, waiting. I can't take off my shirt, I just can't. Mum hasn't bought me a bra yet. I can't even close my eyes, it's like there are matchsticks stuck in them. Dad walks over, now he's unbuttoning my shirt and it's all messed up in the wet sand where he dropped it and I can feel my face melting, as people stare. An eleven year-old girl, in just her knickers. I want to explode, my head feels like it's exploding, and I want to be three again, to make this okay. I run into the water, smell the tainted sea air and dive under the paralysing grey. I'm sure I can taste my own blood, feel it burning icy hot in my shrunken chest.

I go further out, but I can still hear the clicking of the camera round his neck. I turn and looked straight at him, the flash burning in my eyes and then I fling myself back into the crying sea. Further out, further out, so I don't have to go back in. The shore disappears, water drags me, and I try to go back to Nan's at Christmas, holding my breath as the water turns warm and red and grows sofas and a Christmas tree and starts to smell of cinnamon and spiced apple. I can't hear anything apart from a far-away, whooshing goodbye. Nan walks in the door to tell me dinner's not ready yet, did I want to go back home for a bit? I said could I just stay, everyone would be here eventually anyway, but she was shouting at me, 'wake up for Christ's sake' and pushing me in the chest, out the door and into the cold; snowballs explode inside my bones, marrow freezes.

I convulse, nearly head-butt some woman full of energy and leaning very close.

She's saying things, but all I can hear is the sea in my

ears, sloshing and immediate. I'm covered up under something crinkly and silver and she's pulling me upright; everything is super intense and blurry all at the same time and everything means more. She asks me who that man in the doorway is, and it's Dad but I don't want to say that right now, so I just say nothing.

Later, they ask me all the W questions. Who am I? I'm Clary. Why was I so far out? What was I trying to do? I said I was swimming to the end of the pier, but they tell me they found me way past the end of the pier so I pretend to be happy I made it back. But mostly: who is that man? In the end, I tell them, so then they change to a new set of questions, and someone finally asks if he's ever hurt me and pinpricks start up my legs and my head shrinks, so all I can see are the chapped lips of the woman in front of me, moving so slow round a piece of gum. I can smell the stale mint of old gum, can nearly taste it. There's a hand on my leg briefly and I jump but it's only hers and her eyes are wide and pretend, only human and not really helping. They could never really help.

'No. Dad's good. He's a good Dad. We're on holiday. I love our holidays.'

The woman stretches her old gum out with fingers and teeth and looks to her right, there's an old man there I didn't notice before, a policeman. He thinks he knows what he's doing and moves closer, makes his voice go like rough honey because that's what the training course told him to do, to make me feel secure and he says, 'You're safe here; we won't send you back if it means you won't be.'

I tell them over and over again that I'm fine. They ask why I wasn't wearing a top and I say it must have come off in the sea, I forgot my swimming suit, and Dad is fine.

They let me go in the end. Dad is outside hopping up and down, giving it all of the fatherly anger. He picks me up when I walk out and cradles me like a baby, but his chest isn't heaving like mine is, it's a stone chest. The adults talk and Dad uses all his wheedling words so we can go.

I tell him this is the last time. I'm not going away with him again.

I think we're going to Hull next year.

BRING YOUR OWN SUN

Silje Heum

On the day she arrived in Hammersmith, the tube was over-crowded, the sky overcast, and everyone seemed to be in a hurry to get anywhere else. Chloe smiled. So far, London was living up to her expectations, but now she needed to put her bags down and let it surprise her. If she was careful, she had about three weeks worth of cash before she absolutely had to get a job. That was plenty of time to learn how the city worked.

She'd memorised the address, but she picked a note out of her pocket and looked at the directions anyway. None of the street names matched any on the note. She saw a young woman outside Starbucks, sitting with her legs crossed underneath her. She was hunched over a book, holding a cigarette, its long ash threatening to fall. Chloe walked over. 'Excuse me,' she said. The woman moved her head in response, but didn't look up. 'Do you know where is the Abercorn Hostel?'

The woman shook her head and murmured, 'I'm not local'. Chloe didn't know what that meant exactly, but understood it meant 'no'. She glanced at the note in her hand. 'Do you know where is the street called Bute Gardens?'

Evie put a finger by the sentence she was on and looked up at the other woman, then at her luggage. 'No, but look,' she pointed at a Belushi's across the street. 'There's another hostel right there. They could probably help you out, maybe.' The woman smiled brightly, thanked her and started walking toward the traffic lights.

Evie pulled out her phone to check the time. Quarter

past noon. Dorin was already fifteen minutes later than she'd expected him to be. She put her book on the table and looked down at the stack of stickers in her lap. A picture of a thin, dark woman leaned forward on her elbows, her ass in the air, staring at Evie with the kind of big, confident eyes that knew your filthiest fantasies. Not the girl you got if you dialled the number, of course. Evie had never met any of those girls. But this one, in the photo, had been a good model – except for all the tattoos Evie had to Photoshop away. She traced the woman's back with her finger and smiled. This was probably her best one yet. The shadowing was *perfect*.

'What you reading?'

Evie jerked her head up and stared straight into Dorin's usual, stupid grin. She ignored the question. 'Finally,' she said, shoved the stickers at him and stood up.

'Stay for one coffee?' he said.

'Can't. Got an interview at one.'

'For job?'

She shook her head and sat back down. 'Housing co-op. If they accept me I'm finally done sharing rooms.' She smiled at him, unable to hide her excitement. 'It's a good hippy place,' she said. 'Painters and activists and weird theatre people.'

He looked doubtful. 'Where is this?'

'Lewisham.'

He wrinkled his nose.

'What?' she said. 'I saw pictures. Looks really nice.'

'Yeah? Did they put all the black people in the pictures?'

Evie's mouth tightened. She closed her eyes and drummed her fingers on the table, trying to decide how to respond. She picked up her book, dog-eared the page she was on and stood up.

Dorin watched her leave, a grin growing on his face. He preferred when Evie lost her temper, but he enjoyed the silent walk-away, too. He took Evie's stickers for a leisurely walk, vaguely north then west, as the clouds darkened above him. He was not in a hurry. Though he knew the next time he got caught he would be deported, he enjoyed the part of his job that involved defacing public property. So he sauntered around Chelsea and Notting Hill, sticking lewd advertise-ments all over their phone booths, public bathrooms, on ashtrays outside pubs. He even left a few on the hood of a car he thought looked particularly expensive. Eventually he ran out of stickers and, by a ridiculously circuitous route, reached the southwest gates of Kensington Gardens. He found a bench inside; the moment he sat down, rain started pouring.

He watched people open up umbrellas or run for cover, but stayed put himself. He'd been reading books about being present, awake, and receptive. About being a receptacle. He emptied his head of thoughts. He closed his eyes to better feel the rain – unusually heavy for English rain, he thought – and then forgot all about not thinking. Instead he thought maybe he should change jobs; maybe that was it. He thought maybe he'd like to be an airline pilot, or a bouncer. He thought maybe he didn't like where he lived. Maybe he'd even be willing to live east, if Evie lived with him. Maybe Evie would marry him and become a famous photographer, in that order, and then she would buy a house for them in some Swiss mountain village where he would garden and throw pebbles in the little river behind their house while waiting for her to return from whatever exciting job she was on at the moment, and eventually, in the end, maybe he would die first. He opened his eyes and stared straight up into the rain. He thought maybe he should go back to Mar-seilles, try the Legion again.

An umbrella blocked his sight and suddenly Victor was sitting down next to him. Without looking at Dorin, he muttered, 'Fucking idiot, you're soaked.'

Dorin smiled. 'I was thinking before too, that if you

curse less you will maybe become less angry.'

Victor ignored the advice. He squinted sideways at Dorin, jigging his knee compulsively. 'I will give you back on Friday,' he said.

Dorin shrugged and fished his wallet out of a pocket. 'What you need it for anyway? You earn more than I do.'

'Rent.'

Dorin laughed. 'Where you pay rent?'

Quick, tight smile. 'Okay. Food.' He grabbed the twenty-pound notes out of Dorin's hand and left him there in the rain.

Victor got on a bus toward Waterloo, but halfway along Oxford Street he was already so fed up with the afternoon traffic that he decided to walk instead. Victor hated the tube as much as he hated tourists – and by 'tourist' he meant anyone enjoying a stroll in central London. He made it as far as Leicester Square, saw the pink and purple lights outside the Empire, and found himself walking into the casino like it was planned all along.

He bought his chips at the table. The croupier started the spin and launched the ball. Victor didn't calculate probabilities. He didn't look at the board with the recent winning numbers. Betting on hot numbers was just as dumb as believing cold numbers were due.

He put the whole stack of chips on the number seven, because why prolong the misery when a straight-up bet could give you the outcome in thirty seconds? The croupier said no more bets, the ball slipped into its slot, and Victor didn't watch it. Obviously he had lost; you always lost.

He waited for the croupier to place the dolly somewhere in his field of vision – which eventually the croupier did, on number sixteen. Victor felt oddly satisfied, having his pessimism confirmed. The familiar urge to leave London grew in him. He'd made it here with just a backpack and determination. Why wasn't that enough to make it back out?

Victor grinned at the other players and headed toward

the toilets. He slammed open the door, and stood staring at his own reflection until the bathroom attendant said, 'Okay, sir?' Victor looked over at the man, in his waistcoat and tie, guarding the paper towels. His placid face and polite tone made Victor want to punch him. Instead, he just stared for a few moments. Then he turned away.

Janos watched the man slam the door open and walk out. His face didn't change. He stood stolid, disinterested - and he ached. Feet, back, pride, something growing in his gut. He offered people soap and towels and thanked them for the tip. He looked at his wristwatch every twenty minutes, and he smiled exactly as wide and often as strictly necessary. When his shift ended, he sat down and calculated his expected wages. He considered getting a bike to save money on transport then remembered he was terrified of traffic.

Outside it was dark, and snowing. The ground was wet. He caught the last tube back to Abercorn and found the reception closed. He let himself in a side door with his key card, climbed up the fire escape toward his room and stopped on the third level. He didn't want to go inside. He'd recently moved into a room with five Romanian construction workers; he was the new guy, the odd one out, and it seemed to him that they tried to make sure he felt it. So he stayed there on the fire escape, looking out over Hammersmith, though there was nothing really to see from where he stood, except the bus station. He looked down at the wall surrounding the hostel, at the torn plastic bag hanging off the barbed wire, and the knot in his stomach grew louder.

A woman came crashing through the door, a cigarette between her lips. She was maybe twenty, wearing pyjama pants and a too-tight vest. She noticed Janos looking at her, smiled widely and said, 'Alright?'

Janos hesitated. 'It's my birthday today,' he said eventually, and wondered why he hadn't just said 'fine'.

The woman seemed genuinely excited. 'That's *amazing!*'

Janos wasn't sure he agreed. 'Yeah,' he said. Though really it was just a thing that kept happening to him every year.

'How old are you? Oh, wait – '

'Thirty.'

'Wait, I have some wine.' She disappeared back through the doors, and Janos sat down on the steps. A few seconds later she returned with a bottle and two coffee mugs. She sat down next to him and beamed. She poured. He watched. 'Faustino,' he said. She looked puzzled. He leaned over her legs and tapped the bottle with a fingernail. 'Rioja.' He looked up at her, smiling. 'This is where my family lives.'

She smiled back. She handed him a mug and said, 'Here. Happy birthday.'

They sat sipping their wine in silence for a while, watching big, fat snowflakes fall in the light of a street lamp below them. Chloe offered him a cigarette, which he declined, then lit her own. The snow had started to settle now, but neither of them expected it to stay very long.

IMAGINARY PLACES

Sean Wai Keung

The night before the morning
the ambulance turned up
I watched internet streams
from random webcams on
random streets in cities I didn't
know existed. Keetmanshoop, Namibia.
Ufra, Turkmenistan. Arlington, USA.

Each time a person or car or animal
moved jaggedly past the lens I took a shot
of tequila & drew a thin black X on my arm.
I didn't sleep.

So when the ambulance came to
pick her up in the morning & I
rode with them that siren sound
blurred blue/white/yellow/neon
red meaning blood & danger &
love tube noise beep beep beep
the smell of metal sterile bleach latex
glove sniff sniff sniff it all melted
inside me & formed a jellyfish
whose tentacles wrapped around my brain.

& even today I can still
hear that white coat
speak: calm down calm
down son you aren't in one of those
imaginary places now & I say back

who is driving & do they know the
way the streets are awfully busy tonight.

OBSCENE ART

Sean Wai Keung

Gary took a chair & threw it through his window.
The chair (a smelly antique with faux leather seats)
used to provide him with support but then he outgrew it
& nothing was left but spilled coffee stains & an arse print.
He had started to see it as a metaphor for his mother
before he threw it through his window.
The window had kept him safe but also locked him in.
It was the perfect metaphor for his social anxiety.

So in other words
Gary threw his mother through his social anxiety. He was
shortly arrested for this.

Gary's mother read about the incident in the morning papers
The headline:

GARY ARRESTED FOR SPONTANEOUS PERFORMANCE OF
VIOLENTLY METAPHORICAL PHYSICAL POETRY

She went to visit him in prison.

'Why did you do it, son?' she asked from behind
    bulletproof glass.

Gary refused to speak to her. 'I don't talk to chairs,' he told
    the guard
before walking back to his cell.

Later that night, he stared at the cracked bricks in the walls
until they started to remind him of his childhood hopes & dreams.
He looked at his bed & saw a bug-infested attempt at comfort.
A perfect metaphor for his father.

He eventually spent ten years on death row
before he was sent
to the electric chair.

JUST GAMES
Nanou Blair Gould

Pollen clung to Sonny Jim's shabby black fur. Like down, Monty thought. Sonny barked and trotted out from beneath the apple tree.

And then his head exploded.

Monty dropped his slingshot. He couldn't scream because his tummy and heart and lungs all seemed to have squeezed themselves into his throat and because, if he screamed, the hot purple thing sliding down his cheek would slide into his mouth.

The ugly stump of Sonny Jim's neck pumped blood into the earth and Monty felt the grass turn soggy beneath his toes. Sebastian dropped out of the apple tree, cradling the rifle to his naked chest. He walked over and stood beside the dog.

'Is he dead?'

Monty nodded miserably. Seb squatted beside Sonny's body and put a hand on his flank.

'I almost got you.'

Monty nodded again. He wiped the slimy purple thing off his cheek with the back of his hand. He was shivering badly despite the heat.

'I didn't see him,' said Seb. 'You know I was aiming at the apples. You know that, don't you, Monty?'

'Yes,' said Monty.

'You were shooting apples too.'

Monty had only used the rifle once. The stock had bruised his collarbone, but a rotten brown firework had burst across the lawn, even though Seb swore he would never hit an apple on his first go. After that, Seb had confined him to the slingshot. And now Sonny Jim's head lay strewn across the lawn.

'Should we t-tell your mum?'

'No,' said Seb. 'She's not here, anyway.'

'W-what do we d-do?'

'Stop your teeth chattering, I can't think.'

Seb pulled the collar from Sonny's neck and rubbed it clean in the grass.

'Call the v-vet?'

'The vet can't make dead dogs come alive again, Monty.'

Monty crouched on the ground and put his face between his knees. He didn't want Seb to see him cry.

'Don't cry,' said Seb. 'That's stupid. He was my dog and I shot him.'

'I know,' Monty sniffed. He wiped his nose on the hem of his shorts. Seb always said people who cried were stupid. Seb never cried. Neither did his twin, Adelaide. Monty wished he wasn't stupid, but he couldn't help it.

Seb put a hand on Monty's shoulder and Monty sniffed hard and stood up. Seb tugged the strap from around his neck and held the rifle out to Monty.

'I need you to take this back to Dad's shed,' he said.

'I-I don't want to touch it.'

Seb didn't say a word. He held the rifle out in front of him and looked at Monty.

'I don't want to, Seb.'

'If you want to be my friend you have to help me, Monty. Else we'll get into trouble with the police.'

The police. Monty hadn't thought of that. It was bad enough worrying how angry Seb's mum and dad would be when they found out. He couldn't imagine Seb's mum getting angry. Just that morning she'd made them pancakes on the Aga with strawberries and maple syrup and called him poppet, same as she called Seb and Addie. He supposed that Seb's mum never got angry with Seb because she didn't know the things he got up to.

'Don't let anyone see you,' said Seb. 'Nobody can know.'

Monty nodded. He took the rifle by the strap so the barrel swung down. He left Seb with Sonny Jim's body and hurried across the lawn, pollen clotting between his sticky red toes. How had their exhilarating game of pirates become so terrifying?

Monty paused by the wall between the two gardens to make sure nobody was passing the gate. Nobody was. He darted across the gravel and pulled the shed door open. The air inside washed over him like a cool, damp flannel. He relished the stink of petrol after the smell of Sonny's fur baking on the front lawn. He clambered onto the old mower and slung the rifle on its hook at the back of the shed. Then he hopped down and kicked the door shut.

Halfway back to the wall he saw Adelaide standing on the kitchen porch, sipping a glass of water.

'Hello Monty,' she said.

'Hi Addie,' said Monty.

Addie looked just like Seb but with curly brown hair that she plaited and tied with silver hair bands. She was wearing a white summer dress.

'Where's Seb?' she asked.

'Out the back,' said Monty. 'We're playing.'

Addie peered at Monty over the rim of her glass.

'What's that on you?'

'Paint,' Monty said quickly. He and Seb had painted brown and green stripes on their cheeks and nipples before stealing the rifle from the shed. 'It's camouflage.'

'No,' said Addie. She stepped down from the porch and walked up to him. She touched his cheek and they peered at her fingertip, red and slick.

'I heard a gun.'

Monty shrugged. He couldn't lie to Addie any more than he could lie to an adult.

'Where's Sonny Jim, Monty?'

'Seb shot him.'

Addie went very quiet. She looked at Monty the same way Seb had when he held out the rifle, then she pinched him hard on his bruised collarbone.

'Liar! I know you are.'

Monty shook his head, his eyes filling with tears again. And though Addie hissed 'You're lying Monty, you're lying!' over and over again, he knew she knew he wasn't, because she was crying too. She sat on the grass and wept into her fists. Monty didn't tell her she was stupid for crying because he knew she wasn't. He stood over her, telling her it had been an accident, that they had been shooting apples, Sonny Jim got in the way, then Seb called, 'Monty!' from the back garden and Addie looked up at Monty, her eyes pink and wet.

'I want to see him,' she said.

'I don't think you should.' Monty paused. 'It's disgusting. His head exploded.'

'I don't care. Where is he?'

Monty led Addie back to the apple tree where Seb crouched, smoothing out a tarpaulin sheet. When he saw Addie, he stopped. Addie stared at Sonny's headless body for a moment, then at her brother.

'Sorry, Addie,' said Seb.

They gazed at each other, neither looking sad, nor angry, nor anything. Then Addie nodded and Seb went back to smoothing out the sheet.

'I'm going to put Sonny on here so we can move him better,' he said. 'Monty, I need you to pick up all the smaller pieces and put them in that bucket and then we'll wash the grass with the hose.'

Monty gathered up all the pieces in the grass as Seb said. When he finished, he hurried to the fence and threw up his pancakes into the grass the other side, but he didn't cry. Seb had dragged Sonny onto the tarpaulin and was wrapping him up while Addie unravelled the hosepipe. They

rinsed down the grass and their feet then Addie wet her
hand and rubbed Monty's face clean of blood and paint.

'Are we burying him?' Monty asked.

'There's no time,' said Seb, 'Mum and Dad will be home
soon.'

'Well we can't take him out of the gate, else everyone
will see,' said Addie. She turned to her brother. 'Just so you
know, if they catch us, I won't pretend like I don't know you
killed Sonny.'

'They won't catch us,' said Seb. 'We'll take him into the
field. Everyone knows Reverend Guffries hunts pheasants
and foxes. Mum doesn't like us playing in the garden when
the sun goes down because that's when he's out with his
gun.'

'Won't he get into trouble?' asked Monty.

'No,' said Addie. 'He's a Reverend. God will forgive him.'

'Let's make a hole under the fence. It'll look like Sonny
sneaked out and got accidently shot.'

The children set to work, scraping a hole in the soil
with their fingers, then taking it in turns to wriggle through,
buckling the wire enough for a big dog like Sonny Jim to
squeeze through. Addie took off her white summer dress to
help. She ran into the field in her underwear, to check that
the Reverend wasn't about. Seb pushed the tarpaulin bundle
under the fence and Monty pulled it onto the bank. Together they carried Sonny into the field.

'Here will do,' said Seb. He unwrapped the sheet and
dragged his dog into the long grass. Addie stood and hugged
her chest and Monty cried a little. One at a time, the twins
crouched to kiss Sonny Jim's soft tummy, still flecked with
tufts of pollen, placed his collar by the stump of his neck
and scattered the bucket of meat into the grass around him.
An ear flopped over Monty's foot – the funny one that always hung at an angle – and Seb flicked it off with his toe.

'Don't worry, Monty,' he said.

Monty wasn't worried. He felt guilty and miserable and

even a little bit sorry for Reverend Guffries.

'Will God forgive *us*?' he asked.

'Of course He will,' said Addie. 'We're innocent. We're children.'

Seb crumpled the tarpaulin into the bucket and held Addie's hand with his free hand and Addie held Monty's and slowly, quietly, they walked back to the fence.

Before they could reach the bank, they heard the screeching of a gate and tyres crunching gravel. Seb and Addie scrambled to the fence and were through faster than rats, but Monty grabbed a thistle in his haste to follow, squealed and stumbled back into the grass.

'Monty, crawl to the hedge!' Seb hissed.

Monty crouched as small as he could. He felt so frightened; he wished he still had his slingshot to feel more like a pirate.

'I can't!'

'You *have* to. If they see you, they'll think you killed Sonny.'

But he hadn't! Oh, it was unfair. Seb was his best and most exciting friend but he did some very bad things. Monty crawled forward, sobbing. He wiped a tuft of pollen from his nose. He thought of pink Calpol and of his mother, tenderly wiping his face with a tissue.

Another bang, and Monty was dead.

The twins sat on the windowsill, picking at marmite sandwiches, watching the paramedics lift the little grey bundle containing Monty's body into the ambulance. When Monty's parents arrived, Seb slid onto his bed and said to Addie, 'Come away from there.'

Addie pushed her crusts through the crack in the window, forgetting Sonny wouldn't eat them up anymore.

'Will you tell the truth?' asked Addie.

'What truth?' said Seb. 'Reverend Guffries killed Monty by accident, when he was out hunting.'

'You killed Sonny Jim.'

Seb sat up and snatched one of Addie's plaits in his fist. Addie toppled from the sill, twisted around and grabbed a handful of her brother's blonde curls.

'It was just a game.'

'But it's not a game anymore, is it? It's lies.'

'What about you? Are you going to lie for me, Addie?'

'No,' said Addie. 'I'm going to pretend I don't know any-thing.'

Seb let go of Addie's hair and Addie let go of his and climbed back onto the windowsill.

'Look,' said Addie, 'from up here you can pretend they're dead birds.'

Seb climbed up beside his sister. The patch of grass where Monty and Sonny had lain was thick with pink pollen, soft and white as down.

STAR THEORY

Victoria Stevens

That summer was the last one I spent at the lake house. It would've happened sooner or later. I'd already begun to outgrow the long, lazy days spent on the jetty fishing or reading by the water.

'Look out for your Grandpa, Daniel,' Mum said, as she dropped me off outside. 'You don't have to be fragile to break.'

Grandpa slept a lot that summer. He hadn't done much else since Nanna died, but it still made me feel helpless. 'A family just bought the cabin next door,' he said between naps on my second day there, eyelids drooping again. 'They've a son your age. You should introduce yourself.'

I spotted him for the first time next morning, down on the faded wood of the jetty by the lake. He was a spindly boy with too much hair and the palest skin I'd ever seen. I didn't know then how easily and how often he could spend hours stood on the shore, just staring out at the water. The next day he was out on the jetty again. I made my way down and came to a stop beside him. He was hunched over a sketchbook, scribbling furiously, his feet dangling off the side of the decking and into the murky brown water beneath.

'Hello,' I said finally. 'I'm Daniel.'

'Ruben,' he said, without looking up. His skin was so fair, I could see faint, bluish veins through his eyelids, his eyelashes so long they brushed his cheek. 'Star-sign?'

I blinked down at him. 'Sagittarius?'

He raised his head and looked at me with sharp, dark eyes. 'Aries. You can sit, if you want.' He scooted over to make space for me beside him.

The stars were Ruben's thing, it turned out. He knew them by heart, every one catalogued in the back of his mind with all the little details – like how big they were and when they shone the brightest. I'd seen people with hobbies before, sports teams and films, but never quite like Ruben. Never quite so all-consuming.

That first day, he told me he was sure humans could read the stars like some read palms. He'd almost figured it out, he said, the way to tell your future from the constellations. He was convinced our lives were already mapped out up there, detailed in the galaxies. That everything was carved into the sky before we were even alive. Part of some grander plan. I'd never been a big believer in fate, but the way Ruben talked about it made me wonder.

One day when we were out on the jetty and he was showing me his notebook full of lines and patterns, I asked him what his future looked like. He just shrugged, a little smile playing on his lips.

'It doesn't look like anything.'

Ruben wasn't just interested in the stars. He was so fixated that he couldn't talk about anything else for long; not without bringing the conversation back round. It should have been irritating, but I only found his enthusiasm endearing. His favourite constellation was Eridanus, he told me, leading me around the lake one night. The sky over the water was so much darker than in the city and the moonlight turned the sand a ghostly white, but what I remember most was how soft his voice was, filled with the sort of warmth people reserve for the things they love. He pointed out the other constellations: Andromeda and Sagittarius and Orion. I listened closely. I don't know at what point that summer I stopped paying attention to the words and just concentrated on the sound of Ruben's voice, but it was probably about the same time I caught myself thinking about what his lips tasted like.

The sudden awareness that Ruben was a boy and still

made my heart pound came from nowhere, but it didn't
scare me. Maybe it was because he was so different from
anyone else I'd known, too. Sweeter, softer. More gentle. He
was a contradiction, one second full of light and energy and
the next, closed off completely. He told me he was empty,
that he was a supernova and everything around him just disappeared. Sometimes he would reach out for me for no
reason, cold fingers curling around my arm, as if I was the
one solid thing he could hold onto. I think he needed help,
but didn't know how to ask for it.

'How far do you think you could get?' he asked me in
my third week at the lake house, the two of us sitting with
Grandpa's fishing rods in the water, waiting for one of the
catfish to bite.

'How far, where?'

'If you went in the water and you just kept on walking
and you didn't stop?'

'I don't know,' I frowned. At the time it didn't strike me
as an odd question. It was the kind of question that was normal in Ruben-world. 'Maybe halfway?'

'Halfway,' he echoed, and there was a determination in
his voice that made my chest ache.

One Wednesday, he never showed, so I went to find him.
His mother told me to head on up to his room and so I did,
pausing outside to collect myself before I knocked and
pushed the door open.

The room was dim, the curtains drawn against the sun.
Ruben was hunched over the desk, back to the door, with
just a desk lamp for light. His whole body went stiff when I
stepped inside.

'Mum, I'm working!' he snapped, shielding the papers
on his desk from view. 'Get out!'

'It's just me.'

'Oh,' he said softly, turning in his chair to look at me,
the lamp casting shadows that danced on his face.

I looked around his room. Every inch was covered with sketches and diagrams and astrology charts, layered over one another in a strange collage. The floor and the bed were flooded with discarded sheets of paper, all of it covered in bright red ink.

'I-I'll come back later,' I stammered, and turned on my heel before he could ask me to stay.

There is something very odd about fear, something strange about the way it lives inside you. I watched as the dark smudges under Ruben's eyes turned a livid purple. His right eye began to twitch one afternoon and never stopped. I listened to his incoherent mumblings about the alignment and the position of the sun and the moon and I said absolutely nothing. My gut said run and don't look back, but I was too invested not to stay.

His star theory had taken hold.

He spent hours taking me through his sketchbook. The position of Monoceros meant that he was going to sleep well that night. The brightness of Hydrus meant he was going to lose something. His predictions became increasingly outlandish. His scribbles tore the paper clean in two. I should have told him to stop, that he was wrong – that they were just lines in a book and they didn't mean anything – but I couldn't find the words. The stars meant too much to him, and Ruben meant too much to me, to take them away.

'I'm going to die,' he announced at the close of the fifth week.

'We're *all* going to die eventually, Ruben.'

He shook his head. 'Not eventually. Not when I'm old. Not just one day.'

'What are you talking about?'

'I've seen it. I've figured it out down to the very day.'

The air was still, the surface of the lake impossibly smooth, and Ruben's voice was the calmest I'd ever heard it. There was something heavy in his expression, something dark in his eyes, and I couldn't breathe. Was that what he'd meant before, when he'd said his future didn't look like any-thing?

'I'm going to die,' he said again, with an even, eerie clarity.

'When?'

'Soon,' he said, and turned his head toward the lake.

The last night I spent in Ruben's company was a pivotal one. We went to our usual place on the jetty and as we talked he cradled my hands gently in his own, tracing the fine lines of the constellations into my palm with soft fingertips. I'd wanted to kiss Ruben a lot that summer, but never more than that night. Caught in the moonlight, I knew that all our days had been leading to that moment.

'Go on,' he said softly, moving closer, like he could feel the way my eyes never left his mouth.

I envied him so much, how sure he was. How sure he was of who we were. Ruben was the first boy I ever kissed and I knew the second our lips touched that no one else would ever measure up. He was a supernova after all, and not because he was so fascinating or beautiful or impossible, but because he burned too bright and any moment now he would implode and destroy everything he touched, myself included.

'I'm leaving in the morning,' he breathed after, fingers laced with my own. 'Come with me.'

'To where?'

'Anywhere,' he said giddily. 'Nowhere. Let's just go! Let's just go together. It's time. Come with me.'

I was so scared I couldn't catch my breath, and all I could do was nod.

I didn't sleep that night. I lay awake instead, waiting for the tap at the window. It came just after dawn as Ruben promised it would, when the sunlight was still weak, and made me cold.

I told him I couldn't go with him before he had a chance

to speak, that it was his destiny to follow and not mine, *his* fate written in *his* stars. The real truth was that it was just too big, too much. I wanted to follow him, but I didn't know how. He was way ahead of me, and I couldn't catch up. I wished I shared his faith, but all I saw when I looked at the constellations were balls of gas burning themselves out of existence, a million light years away. I'm not you, I wanted to say. I'm not that strong.

'You said you'd come!' His eyes were huge. 'You said you'd come with me! I don't want to go alone!'

I stayed resolute, even though I wanted to reach through the open window and beg him to stay. But Ruben would never have chosen me over his destiny. He could tell my mind was made up. I felt it in the way he recoiled from me, the distance between us suddenly vast even though he was still close enough to touch. I watched him walk away for the last time. I found an envelope outside my window later that day, packed full of his sketches. All of his stars and patterns and theories, detailed and preserved in graphite.

These are yours now, he'd written on the front.

It took four days of Ruben being missing before anyone came to the lake house. The police came first, with their clipboards and questions, and then eventually the forensics guys with their white suits and their oxygen tanks.

'Antares is especially bright tonight,' I said to Grandpa absentmindedly as we watched them scour the lake from the window.

'What does that mean?' he asked.

'Nothing,' I said, Ruben's stars heavy in my back pocket. 'It means nothing.'

I left the lake house the next day and I didn't look back. He was the first boy I ever kissed, the first boy I ever loved, and one day, when I can close my eyes without picturing his face, there might be another.

I only hope he started walking and never, ever stopped.

HEADWARE

[EXTRACT FROM A NOVEL]

Jo Schinas

Besides Xanthe, twenty-eight people are present at the party. Xanthe knows the height of the twelfth-floor flat is forty metres. She knows how far it is above sea level, too.

The furniture should fold out of the walls, but some of it has seized in open position permanently, the cooker and the table for instance, and some of it won't fold into place at all any more, the seats being the most inconvenient example. One of the blinds has unfurled as it's supposed to – the others, stuck, expose squares of semi-dark night sky. Xanthe can see the stars, even in the light-polluted city. Not that she looks at them a lot.

The hosts have added some stand-alone chairs – bits of broken office furniture, a sofa that's spilling its stuffing everywhere. But most people, including Xanthe, have to make do with the floor even so. Beside her, a bloke with blond dreads has been dozing for a while. Tobacco smoke hangs thick in the room already; Xanthe's cigarette adds more. She can smell each of the components in the smoke. Not just the tar and the nicotine, but the hundreds of smaller elements also.

A group of three, one girl and two guys, have been jamming in the kitchen area for a while. They've turned themselves up too loud for this space. Xanthe thinks she's seen the singer before. It's the mike doing most of the singing, as is standard these days, and the guy's rigged up the settings so they make a howl of his voice. It's not that she's seen him, she realises, more that she's seen versions of him before. His hair arranged in disarray. His jacket thrown on carefully. That type.

Xanthe knows the name of every note; she knows where it fits in its scale. She could compose music that would move people, if she wanted to. It's simply an effect of pitch and pace. Music hasn't ever moved her.

'I've a friend you ought to talk to.' Chrissi-Rose plumps herself down beside Xanthe. Her pink miniskirt matches her pink afro. 'Might be a job in it. He needs you to find somebody.' She puts her drink on the floor and fluffs her hair. From her neck dangles the diamanté external drive, filled with favourite memories, that she wears all the time.

'Needs me to trace a username? Then I'll talk to him online, not here.'

Chrissi-Rose likes to throw parties. Sometimes she persuades Xanthe to come. When the two first met – through friends, casually, a couple of years ago – each suspected the other of working on the undernet, where all users have anonymity and illicit trade thrives. When an alias rips off an undernet site – perhaps a marketplace, where hookers or dealers or killers tout their services – the boss needs an address to send his heavies to. So Chrissi-Rose and Xanthe trace undernet usernames to their sources. Chrissi-Rose has a position with a single large site. Xanthe, who's freelance, takes on Chrissi-Rose's difficult cases. She is, after all, at an advantage.

'Uh, no. It's not like that.' Chrissi-Rose hesitates. 'OK, look, he had this girlfriend who disappeared about four years ago.'

'So she's who he needs me to find? Come on, Chrissi, that's not what I do.'

'I know, I know, but he's a mate of mine. It's not so far off what you do.' Chrissi-Rose's voice changes to a pleading one. A mere matter of tonal modification. 'You're smart. You're supposed to be some super-robot, for fuck's sake. So don't tell me you can't do it if you want to.'

'Not a robot. Technically. And I don't want to. The girl's

probably been buried in a landfill for the last four years anyway.'

'At least talk it over with Jude.' Chrissi-Rose rises. 'And leave off the bit about the landfill.'

'Wait,' says Xanthe. But Chrissi-Rose is off looking for her friend already.

Xanthe sighs through her nose. She drains her drink and stands up to look for another one, stepping over the dreadlocked bloke. The band seems to have stopped for good this time. Some people are on headware in the corner. Interfaces between mind and machine, first invented for therapy. Headware was created to move memories and dreams onto devices for shrinks to study; then as the technology developed, information transfer moved the other way. The headsets soon arrived in homes. The earliest let you download edited, auto-enhanced memories to devices so they wouldn't fade. Then the movie industry got in there, and the gaming industry too, combining dreams and CGI into virtual experiences. Then self-help headsets, that delivered a dose a day.

The bunch in the corner are on home-modded sets, the effects above every legal boundary. In the past, Xanthe headtripped her fair share. You keep at it, though, you'll kill yourself that way.

One of the headtrippers has been giving off a high giggle for some time. A vein's burst in his eye.

Chrissi-Rose comes back, singer behind her. This must be the friend.

'Hey, Xanthe,' she says. 'Meet Jude.'

'Jude. Hello.'

'Hey.' He shakes her hand. 'Chrissi-Rose said you help your clients find people? You're, like, a detective?'

'You could put it that way.'

'And, uh...you're a robot, right, too? You don't mind me...?'

'Biobot. Technically. Human mostly, in body anyway, but my head's half-full of machinery.'

She's learned to summarise herself in a sentence. It's too

much effort to take offence every time.

'Wow.'

'It's based on sets like those.' She gives the lot in the corner another glance. 'Inbuilt computer with an inbuilt interface.' She adds this fun fact occasionally.

'Inbuilt computer? Does that include, I dunno, inbuilt net access?' He laughs. 'That's a step up from eyeware. Seriously – I'd have that done.'

'Yeah, that's one feature. But they start putting it in at the embryonic stage. You'd end up dead if you had it done at your age, or at least insane.'

'Shame. So you've always...so, well, why were you made?'

'I'm ex-military.'

'You're – wow. Were you, like, a spy? You don't look old enough to have been through the military.'

'As to what I was, I've no idea. They wiped me when they discharged me about six years ago. And I don't know my inset date, since they've classified my previous life. Hey, maybe they kicked me out early.' Chrissi-Rose has spotted somebody else and wandered off, leaving them alone. Now would be the time to retreat casually, before Jude can return to business. 'Well, I'm off to look for another drink.'

'But, wait. I have to tell you about this problem of mine. Chrissi-Rose said you could help me.'

'Yeah...listen, Jude, it's not the sort of job I do.'

'In four years, the police have got nowhere – I mean, I doubt they're even trying by this stage. To them, Lola's just another name on a file, just one more unsolved case.'

'Well, the interval doesn't exactly make it easier. You've left this a bit late.'

'I found somebody else, after Lola, somebody who helped me through that whole time. We broke up a few months ago. And then it came to me, that I'll always be waiting for Lola, that I won't be happy with anybody till I know what happened to Lola— '

'OK. Spare me.' The party's thinning; it's long past late.

'Think I'm going to say goodbye.'

'Xanthe!' Chrissi-Rose is back, tipsy and weaving. 'Where you off to?'

'Heading home. I don't think I can do much for Jude here.'

'Xanthe. *Xanthe.*' Chrissi-Rose turns her so they face away from Jude. He hovers, hopeful. 'Wait. It's not all about Jude. *I* need you to find out what happened to Lola.'

'You knew her too?'

'Slightly.'

'Cool. You can help Jude. Chrissi, I track undernet user-names. I leave the lost girlfriends and the lost puppies to those with a sentimental side.' Xanthe prefers to work with computers rather than with people.

Chrissi-Rose lowers her voice a little. 'It's this boss of mine; I don't think he'd approve. See, I'm supposed to work exclusively for his site. Bastard must have hired another tracer to trace *me*. He knows stuff about me.' She pauses. 'Course it could be a she.'

'Jobbing for his competitors and helping Jude aren't the same. You're letting a faceless boss drive you crazy?'

'You're the best person to take this case anyway.'

'I've told you, both of you: no. But, I think you should trace your boss; might give you a hand with that, if you like. Sorry, Jude, but what are the chances Lola's even alive? Night.'

'Wow,' says Jude. 'Don't overdo the sympathy.'

'I don't do sympathy. I'm a robot.' Xanthe turns a smile on him for a moment. 'Biobot, technically.'

Evening, the next day, and Xanthe's smoking slowly on her balcony. She lives in the same Greater-Greater London area as Chrissi-Rose. Fingers, long and pale, lifting and lowering the cigarette. Her skin and her hair are both the same white-blonde shade, though the short spiky hair has a red streak on the right side. She watches with red eyes as the pterodactyls leave the sky. The terries settle in lines on the tops of the tower blocks opposite. They're culled in the city's centre, but many live on its edge, going through the garbage.

She finished a trace today. MrSpeedy, who sold uppers on one of the major marketplaces, had hung onto a list of his buyers' addresses. The trouble with getting old-style substances online is they must be sent physically, which means letting on where you live. Most vendors delete addresses after sending a package, but sometimes they hold onto them, especially near retirement, in order to blackmail the site. If the seller exposes these identities, the resulting arrests ruin the reputation of the marketplace.

Xanthe hasn't left her flat since the party yesterday. Like Chrissi's, her furniture's of the foldout automatic variety. Unlike Chrissi's, it all functions smoothly. The flat is a single: one room adapting itself continually, reduced to six white surfaces when all the components fold away. Xanthe's been sitting straight-backed on the stool in the centre, her mind online, all day. To anybody else, the room would have seemed empty, but her red eyes filled it with icons and symbols and images. Sometimes the eyes read for a while; sometimes they scrolled; sometimes they clicked on links by contracting slightly. Hanging out on forums full of scammers and flashing avatars and slangy terminology, going through all MrSpeedy's communications. American male, twenties to thirties, she'd concluded from his language. She reduced that to specific American states, from hints about weather and altitude. Then she searched the social-network accounts of American males for a matching linguistic style, restricting this geographically and by age range. She did this on the overnet, where the décor was more discreet, where polite notifications popped up constantly, running the search for hours and hours, almost subconsciously. These were the sort of sites where you spent time with your family, where you were called by the name your loved ones recognised. Finally, she had made one Trevor Stubbs her focus; he'd shown the highest similarity to MrSpeedy. It was more than his multiple-exclamation-mark tendency – MrSpeedy and Mr Stubbs liked to quote the same movie lines.

Now her employer will hire locals to check if Trevor Stubbs is the one. He will be. Xanthe knows her stuff. There will be a visitor for Trevor. He'll be warned off; fatally, it's possible. Maybe there'll be a visitor for Xanthe too, some day. He took a risk, this guy; she's taken a fair few of those. Hey, thousands die every day.

The clouds between the tower blocks are red-tinged; real sunsets don't happen here because the city horizon's never visible. As she smokes, Xanthe zooms in on the ptero-dactyls perched opposite. They crouch there, black leather silhouettes, their talons clutching the concrete. Somebody in a lab constructed one, for kicks maybe. Years ago. Every zoo and every museum had to commission a terry, then that boy-band singer bought a pet one, so all the schoolgirls got them too. These days, strays are everywhere. Built as toys, these predators; now discarded. The authorities put up do-not-feed notices. Local news-sites raise the issue repeatedly. People scare each another with stories. *You hear about that terry that stole a baby?*

She stands in her coat, a black leather shape, then casts the cigarette butt off the balcony. It's still falling through the air as she walks inside.

The call wakes Xanthe. It's only six am; since it's October, it's still dark outside. She'd have slept until eight, maybe. She felt burnt out when she went to bed, but she didn't drop off for hours, even so. An after-effect of spending so long on-line. The meat part of her mind can't cope; it starts to mal-function, to overheat, to ache. This so throws the machine part that it refuses to rest, performing deductions over and over. She could only lie there, her head scorched from in-side, strings of numbers searing her mind's eye.

Bleep bleep bleep of the tone, and the name Chrissi-Rose. She neither hears the call nor sees the name – to say she knows them is more accurate. The sound and the words

46

arrive in her mind directly.

'Yeah?' She almost didn't reply, but there must be some reason why Chrissi-Rose, who likes to sleep in half the day, is ringing this early.

'Xanthe. Thank fuck. I hear somebody in my flat.'

'What? You have two flat-mates.'

'No, shut up, it's not them. One's away, and Ant's been out all night – and it doesn't sound like Ant anyway.' Chrissi-Rose's words crackle as she whispers into her wrist-set. 'There's somebody down there. I think I heard the door-lock break. I don't know what to do.'

Xanthe knows she's not about to involve the police. Things have to be heavier than this before their kind involve the police.

'It's that case,' says Chrissi-Rose. 'Jude's case.'

'Huh? How? Wait, though, let's worry about that later. I bet you it's some broke druggie burglar. He'll probably scare easily. Didn't you get a gun, like I'm always telling you to?'

'Yeah, but...uh, thing is, no bullets. Look, I meant to buy some –'

'You're kidding me. You're *kidding* me. You know this area's not safe –'

Chrissi-Rose's voice rises in panicky impatience. 'I can't even shoot, OK, so what use would it be?'

'*Quiet!* So you use the gun to scare the guy, and maybe hit him with the butt if he tries to make trouble.'

'I don't think he's an amateur. That's what I keep trying to say.' Chrissi-Rose pauses. 'Hang on. Haven't heard him for a while. He might be gone.'

'What? You don't think he's an amateur? Chrissi, if you think he's a pro –'

Crashes, and a short scream from Chrissi-Rose. Xanthe sits up; the room brightens in response. Sounds distort, perhaps as the wrist-set – ripped off? – falls to the floor. Further crashes. Silence.

Xanthe stands up and the bed folds into the floor. She

calls Chrissi-Rose back. No answer. She beckons to the wall; dons clothes, a black shirt, black jeans, black boots as they slide out of it one by one. She calls Chrissi a second time. No answer.

She takes the offground to Chrissi's place, moving as fast as she can; she reaches the block in half an hour. Maybe the wrist-set broke in the tussle. Chrissi might be fine. She might have run. Fought and run.

If Xanthe has a friend, it is Chrissi-Rose.

Twelfth floor. Chrissi-Rose's floor. Xanthe strides from the lift into the corridor. The place is lit poorly; several sections of the illuminated walls are dark, and some flicker on and off continually. Chrissi-Rose's front door stands wide. Her flat-mate Ant is talking to a policeman in the hallway. Ant works with headsets and the like, and sells less-than-legal modifications on the side.

Things have to be heavy before their kind involve the police.

'I spent the night at a girl's place.' Ant's words sound shaky. 'She had to head to work, so I came home. Which is when I – well –'

The cop – big balding bloke – notices Xanthe. Ant turns to look too. It's like he's double-dosed on something he shouldn't have. Unfocused stare.

Xanthe rushes inside the flat, one hand thrusting the cop away; a policewoman is busy by Chrissi-Rose's body. It is slouched on the floor, red soaking into the carpet's grey. The policewoman rises. Xanthe swallows; she must record all the details for reference, before she's barred from the crime scene. The position of Chrissi's corpse, the bullet-hole through the left temple...

Trust Chrissi-Rose to fall so carelessly. Her movements had always bothered Xanthe a little, all bigger than necessary, each blending into the next with a sloppy sort of grace. Xanthe couldn't have brought herself to move so irregularly.

Concentrate.

Burn-mark on the forehead, on the right side, that looks like it's from a headset; there isn't much forehead on the left side. A sore red line around each wrist. A fallen chair. Concentrate. No chain on the neck; no external memory drive. The neck's scored as if the chain's been ripped off. Therefore –

'Come on. Come away. I'm sure it's hard to take.' The policewoman's probably been speaking for some time. She grasps Xanthe's shoulder gently.

Let them think she's likely to crack, the cops; they'll leave her alone quicker. But she's OK: she feels colder than before, emptier than ever before. Helps to fool the police, her hands trembling this way. She stares at the hands. She didn't know they could tremble.

The policewoman hands her over to the policeman; he sits her in the lounge, which is full of debris from the party. He'd like to ask her a question or two. She nods.

So why did she come here today?

'Chrissi-Rose called me. She could hear an intruder in the flat.'

Did Chrissi-Rose have any idea who this intruder might be? Does Xanthe have any idea? Can Xanthe think of anything else that could help with the case?

'No,' she says each time.

As she leaves, Xanthe hears him tell the policewoman: 'My guess? Just your average bungled burglary.' He leans out of the door, as she walks to the lift, and shouts: 'You going to be all right? Maybe call a mate, eh? For some company.'

I can't, Xanthe thinks. She's dead.

'I'll be fine.' She steps into the lift.

Concentrate. Chrissi's killer used a headset to download her memories. Burnt her forehead: in a hurry. She would have been alive at the time; he'd tied her to the chair, hence the weals around her wrists. He'd needed her memories, but he'd also needed to hide them from everybody else; or he wouldn't have taken her drive. After downloading the full set directly, he'd ditch it as soon as possible.

A bin's steel canister stands near the exit. Xanthe checks, but there's nothing but a few cans inside. Outside, she spots a brick on the pavement, notes the splinters of metal and of plastic around it. Underneath is Chrissi-Rose's memory drive, smashed flat. The one that hung between her collarbones so long.

Xanthe crouches. She looks at the fragments of Chrissi's life. Up between the tops of the tower blocks, the sky stays a rainless October grey. The composite sound of the city increases with the start of the day; voices, some lifted in anger and others in laughter, drift down from the balconies above. Xanthe sniffs once; her nose is moist, but her synthetic eyes can't cry. The wind shifts the litter on the pavements. Thousands die every day. The dropped wrappers settle.

Xanthe rises. She puts the pieces of the drive into her pocket. She's a robot. She solves, she deduces, she makes sure information make sense.

She has no tears for Chrissi-Rose, so she'll make this make sense.

ACHROMATIC

Karoline Vembre

Grey

I walked through the park. Two children lay on their backs in the grass, a boy and a young girl. They were both dressed in light, white cotton. The boy gave the girl a small push, as if she'd said something silly. They reminded me of my own children. The girl laughed and rolled over onto her stomach. She looked up at me, her face changing from a smile to an expression of shock. She lifted one hand in front of her mouth, and pointed the other up into the air.

White

I found her under water. My mother. She lay on the bottom of the bathtub. White-faced. I lifted her head. I pulled her out. The water hit the floor, hard. Her skin felt like stone, washed soft by wind and sand. Water ran out of her mouth. I called for my dad. I opened her eyes with my fingers. They were filtered, the colours washed faint. Green turning to blue, and a hollow black.

Grey

I looked through her letters, I read her emails, I turned our mattress, I searched her wardrobe, I looked inside all our jars, our boxes and our vases, I hugged her dresses, I called every number on her phone, I slept in the bathtub, I looked through her desk, I searched through her pockets, I sat in her chair, I asked her friends, I talked to her doctor, I read all the documents on her computer, I looked through her internet history, and there, I saw it. She had searched: 'How does it feel to drown.'

Black

The lights were out in our street. Through the dark, I felt my way up the staircase and hung the rope from the railings. Cars passed on the street outside, like lashes of wind. My throat felt sore. I remembered sliding down these railings as a child, my sister and me taking turns, and our mother holding our hands. I placed the rope around my neck. I closed my eyes. I listened to the familiar sound of the creaking walls, which my father had hated, but my mother had loved. My feet were cold against the floor. As I fell, my eyes opened. I saw the lights flickering back on; blinding me with white.

White

I sat on my little brother's bed and I remembered holding him in the hospital, putting his little fingers into my mouth. I remembered having my arms around him, letting him curl up in my bed when he couldn't sleep. I read him horror stories and when he got scared I comforted him.

Grey

I told everyone to stop sending me flowers. Red, blue, white. Every morning they were there outside the front door.

Bound with ribbons. I didn't know what to do with them. I had no room for them. Roses, violets, lilies. I didn't want them, so I buried them in the yard.

White

I swallowed. The white pills were hard in my throat. The sheets loosened from the edges of the mattress and I curled up inside them. I reached for the lighter on the nightstand and lit one of the cigarettes I had taken out of my father's jacket. My brother and I had smoked them in secret for years. The room pulsated with beats from distant music. My mother had painted the walls dark red, like the inside of a pumping heart chamber. I felt myself drifting. There was smoke trapped inside my lungs, spiralling in my chest. I closed my eyes and stopped breathing.

Grey

I spent my nights between waking and sleeping. Dreaming of the house being flooded and of rotting caskets under the ground. I tried not to think, but kept seeing myself, teaching my son how to tie knots on the boat. I woke with splintering pain in the back of my head and sore jaws. I rolled around, sweating and freezing. Remembering how the ropes dug into his skin and how his feet had swayed, just out of my reach.

White

I woke up in the hospital. Sore and numb. My breathing hurt, like my lungs were burnt. I looked at the machines around my bed. Flickering green and blue lights, switches and cables. A screen with a red line, rising and falling, up and down, beat, no beat, beat. The walls were washed-out white, like eggshells. I imagined myself an unhatched bird, inside the warm room. I did not want the door to open.

Grey

I wondered if I'd ever be able to see her sleeping again, without imagining her dead. I'd found her in her mother's room and talked to her for several minutes before I realised how still she was. The doctor told me I was lucky she survived. She seemed so small on the hospital bed. She'd not wanted to eat in the last weeks, and I hadn't wanted to force her. She'd begun wearing the same clothes day and night, all black, and it was strange now, seeing her in the clean white hospital robe. I'd held her hand in the ambulance. Stroked her hair. It was tangled up into a nest at the back of her head. I tried to untangle it, separating the long brown hairs.

White

He walked with his neck bent, his shoulders collapsed, as if his chest was hollow and his bone structure failing. His eyes were grey. He sat at the foot of the bed and put his hand on my ankle, stroking his thumb up and down. I did not want to meet his eyes. I looked out of the window.

Grey

'Please,' I started. Her face was turned toward the window and the sun. She looked more like her mother every day: the pale, dry skin and the sharp jaw. 'You can't leave me to be on my own,' I said. She closed her eyes. I tried to remember how I'd planned to say what I wanted to say. 'Can you promise me,' I began. She frowned like she did when she had a headache. 'That you won't leave me.'

White

I closed my eyes. I could hear him talking, but the words were blurred. My muscles felt tight, sore with tension.
    'We can live for each other,' he said. I opened my eyes. He looked out of the window. 'We can keep each other alive.' His hand clutched my ankle hard.

Grey

'Will you promise me that?' I asked. Her eyes were fixed on my chest. I reached for her hand, small, almost like a child's. She let me hold her, but did not hold me back. 'Will you?' I asked. She nodded once, in a slow movement. I held her wrist. Feeling her pulse into my palm. 'Thank you,' I said.

White

He kissed my cheek before he left, like he and my mother used to kiss my brother and me in turns, at night. I watched him walk out the door and felt that I could hear his steps fading a long time after he left. My body felt heavy, as if the bones in my chest were made of stone. I took the white sheet off the bed and wrapped it over my shoulders. I walked over to the window. There were two children chasing each other outside on the grass.

Grey

I walked across the street and into the park, not thinking

about where I was going. I checked my pockets for cigarettes, but they were missing. Then I saw the boy and the girl.

White

I opened the window. The warm wind found my skin, under the sheets. The boy caught the girl in his arms and wrestled her down, laughing. They rolled in the grass and ended up on their backs, looking up at the sky.

Grey

The little girl pointed her hand up into the air. I followed the children's eyes and saw a big white bird, soaring alongside the hospital wall. The wings fluttered like paper and peeled away from the bird in mid air. White fabric lingered for moment, then glided downwards, as the body unwrapped itself and fell fast and hard to the ground.

A TRAP FOR A MOLE

Charlotte Taverner

A fair. But for who? 'That's not fair.' all because
of they. The them that keeps children inside and under
there, under their mothers patter patter until the potatoes
    are on
the boil inside the pan. Outside is their inside that is
home. A castle in my home. And a moat and a drawbridge.
'But for who?' That's not fair. A trap for a mole
enticing into a box is slippery business. 'Smoke them out
is best.' To push gives less resistance whereas a pull is trust
gone sour. Shoot them in the back of canvas of wheels of
dirt, of 'what will we do about *them*.' Goes straight through
the moat. A drawbridge for sale. *The Fair is coming to town.*
Folded corners catch the ink that runs down
telegraph poles. Non permanent.
'But for who?' The children swarm when the lights are
    on. All
red and swirling and green and spinning and pink and
    clunking
stubbled men hoot and jeer, painted faces on waltz
out of proportion noses, eyes too close together.
The ponies are all locked away in the evening. The town
comes to play. Holding tongues and pay the fair. Farewell
cul de sac. Hello coconut shy and smash a bric a brack.
Tuc-tuc-tack of a generator. Ride clink clunk into action.
'That's the fair!' who's the mole now. Give them a pull
the lever give them a push off the edge of the dodgems
    bumper
static crackles this is the castle inside the walls. Temporary
    concrete –

permanent damage. *Stay off the grass*. And mind out for moles.

Candy floss is wooly but will not keep you warm
'Oh what's fair?' for a mole cannot see. Roll up,
roll up, asking to come closer toward the slithery tricks and
grubby hands. Clever games to be played to catch a duck
is slippery business. Three goes, two goes, one. Better luck
next time says one. Their bellies are yellow, the yellowest of
shades and mucky faces peer out from behind teddy bears.
Rifle targets, they are shooed. All the ponies are put away.
   'Not fair.'

A person or person's whose residence is neither fixed nor
   permanent...

A bag of pick n mix crumpled in horseshit. The whine of a
   motor
Ch-chig ee, ch-chig ee, coming to a halt who goes there. Not
grass, not there. Am the last one, run along now son. In a
friendly tone? 'That's not fair.' No piss off home
leave us, just moles and hills and smoke. Mother
always said don't talk to strangers child. Toothy grin of
   uncle Jack
a rub on the head? It's him, no them. Don't be naïve.
A pat that sends legs homeward along behind the crowds,
   Tap, tap.

'*But I won, I will not give it back.*' Transparent, angry red
   clings to apron frills.
A sting redder than a metal spoon left in a saucepan. 'Go
   now child back to them.'
'It's not fair.'

The fair is coming, they did come they came with their
   wheels
and metal catkins did open and how they all came to see the

them that
gave a fish to a boy. A boy with a fish, the moat the
    drawbridge the castle gates.
No guards? Say you! Where are all the fish?
No one awake. Wet grass seeping into trainers. Leave it here
    shall I?
Say you! Everyone sleeping in trailers. Not the man that's
    not Uncle Jack.
Click-ting clack-ting he walks with a stick, out from his
    castle down metal steps
that don't touch the grass.

Fair's closed boy. Toothy grin more yellow even than bellies
    of the men that cheat
the folk. But not one boy, who won, and won a fish.
Reach out a hand, not for help, reach out a hand not for a
    shake reach out a hand
with a golden fish. A boy with a fish standing, on the grass
    with the moles who
refuse to be smoked out. They take my fish. Don't! Them
    down at the fair. They
keep children at home. Not my mother.

'But that's not fair!' You returnin' my gift. That's when the
    stick hits the bag.

Sound of toffee slapping inside a mouth. The wet grass. A
    fish that missed
the moat. Gasping mouth open the not uncle, uncle Jack
    turns around. Back to
canvas, no toothy grin. Mother would have done the same.
    We are not
so different. Them and they, us and we but the difference
is this. We are not we, but lots of eyes, looking out on them.

A fair. But for who? 'That's not fair.' all because of they

the them that keeps children inside and under. A fish.
    A castle in my home.
A moat and a drawbridge. 'But for who?' That's not fair.
    A trap for a mole?
No need to smoke them out. Farewell cul de sac temporary
    concrete no
permanent damage. Candy floss is wooly but will not keep
    you warm.
Keep off the grass and hold on to a fish. It's only the fair.

PINEWOOD

Emily Parsons

The smell of pine reminds me of my mother. Back when she was happy and her smile wasn't drawn on with lipstick. We had a pine tree in our backyard in Deloraine, Tasmania. I'd sit in the low branches with Mum and we'd read stories and throw pine needles at each other until our fingers were sticky with sap. She'd tap my nose when it was time to go inside. The smell lingered until the next morning.

When I was five there was a huge storm. It lasted for days and ripped a branch from the pine tree that cracked my bedroom window and glittered glass through my sheets. My father got scared the tree would fall on us one night. One afternoon he chopped it down and covered my ceiling in boards he made from the trunk. I cried for a week. I sat by the stump and practiced my reading for Mum until my eyes and the sky were red.

It was Christmas Eve before the millennium when Mum read me my last bedtime story. She read until my eyelids began to droop. She kissed my nose and whispered 'Goodnight mister.' I could only hum in response. She left when my father crashed through the front door and declared he needed his woman. Later, I heard them going at it. Banging on the walls. My father gave a throaty moan that rattled the floorboards. Mum bawled at first, then she was silent.

I thought about running out with my cardboard sword and shield to see what was happening. But all I could do was pull the covers up under my nose and squeeze my eyes until I saw stars. I counted them as I fell asleep.

Christmas morning Mum yanked open my curtains when it

was just light, buttoned me into my best shirt and pulled me to church. I don't remember the service. I remember being upset that I didn't get to wake her by bouncing on the bed. I hadn't even opened my presents yet. She wore makeup so thick, it made her sweat. It rubbed off on the collar of her green dress.

She lingered around the church long after everyone had gone home, cleaning whatever she could. I snuck into the kitchen and ate the leftover cubes of bread. The pastor invited us to lunch. Mum sucked her lip, said no, that she had to get back. She looked like she was going to say something else, then she stopped herself and smiled.

I watched her walk. How her throat was tight and only softened when we opened the front door and found a note from my father saying he'd gone to Jon and Jackie's for lunch. I ran to the presents under the tree. Mum scooped them up before I could tear them apart.

'Not 'til your father gets home.' She tapped my nose and locked the presents in her room.

We had cold ham and boiled potatoes for lunch.

One of my presents was a pile of books I'd seen at the neighbors' garage sale. Atlases and adventure books. They smelled like my Nan's house. I flicked through, found love notes and crumbs jammed between the pages. I smiled at Mum. She handed me my last present, wrapped in newspaper. Flannel pajamas. She made me try them on; started pulling off my clothes.

'Mum.' I wriggled from her hands. 'I'm eight. I can dress myself.'

'Okay then, mister.' She tapped my nose and leaned against her reading chair. The pajama shirt fell to my knees, the trousers were too big. 'Now, I know they're a bit big at the moment, but you'll grow into them.' She smiled. My father nodded and sucked on his beer bottle.

I hated those pajamas. I hated the collar and the way it scratched my neck. I hated the dusty blue material that stained too easy and gave me away on midnight trips to the stump. I hated that I couldn't fit into the pants until I was ten, and the kids at school teased me for wearing a nightie at camp.

I tried to burn them once, just so I could get a new pair. I held my father's lighter to the elbow and melted a hole that went hard like plastic. Then I remembered Mum's face when I first tried them on. The way her eyes crinkled at the corners. The way she wasn't afraid to show her yellow teeth. So I kept them, and wore them every night even though the plastic hole dug into my arm while I slept.

My little sister was born the year after, on October the first. Mum called her Rosa after that lady on the bus who wouldn't get up. My father spat in the corner of the hospital room and said it was a fucking stupid name and he didn't want his daughter named after some fucking black chick. Mum rolled her eyes. He kicked a bin, swore, tore off down the hall. Mum said something about Rosa being as brave as her namesake. I asked her what she meant.

'Oh, nothing.' She sighed and kissed Rosa. I went back to my book about some English kids on a boat with a prince and a talking rat.

Rosa's cot was put in my room. I'd tell her stories I made up from the patterns on the ceiling until my father came in and said go the fuck to sleep. Then he'd leave, slam the door and make Rosa bawl.

As Rosa grew, my father took jobs that pulled him further from the family. Not that I minded. When he was home the house was cold and quiet. Even with the TV blaring you could hear the walls creak.

He wouldn't touch Rosa. He'd barely look at her. He'd glance at her from across the lounge room when he thought Mum wasn't looking. His face looked pained, like the boys on the footy pitch when their nuts get crushed by a bony knee. At birthday dinners, when Nan said Rosa looked just like him, my father'd just sneer and Mum looked like she was about to throw up. Then Aunty Jac would say, 'Oh, but he has Jane's eyes,' and Mum'd smile again.

My father worked in forestry. I thought it was a horrible job, cutting down trees.

Once, I watched from behind my atlas as he packed his things in the kitchen for a job that would take him away for a month or so.

'Have fun murdering trees,' I said when he turned to leave.

He knocked the book into my face. 'Where do you think your fucking precious books come from?' He hauled his swag onto his back and spat in the hallway on his way out. He left a paper cut on my nose that stung like hell and split open when I smiled.

He came home a few weeks early, shaking. A friend had misjudged the height of his tractor and clipped some power lines. He was dead before they could get to him. I watched my father tell Mum. He had tired eyes. Her smirk spread into a smile when he went to have a shower. I'd never seen my mother look that way before. She reminded me of boys who fry ants with a magnifying glass, and squeal as they watch them burn.

The funeral was the day after. Dad staggered home, drunk and white as Nan's fine china. He grabbed a beer, slunk out back. I snuck out behind the hedge to watch the sky turn red around him.

My father sat on the stump of the pine tree. His head rested on his chest and he held the beer in his fingertips. His hands shook. The bottle fell. Beer lapped out of the neck and sank into the earth at his feet. His tears collected and hung from the tip of his nose. He blew air from his cheeks and pinched the bridge of his nose. He shut his eyes and shook all over. He pressed his lips together until his cheeks went red and he moaned into the side of his wrist.

I felt embarrassed, like I'd walked in on someone in the

bathroom, worse, like I was seeing something raw and dirty and private. I crept back inside and tried to shake that moan from my mind.

By the time Rosa turned three, there was no denying she was like our father. Thick brown hair that curled like smoke and skin that browned in the weak spring sun. Even the eyes that Mum had claimed, turned hazel, like his. Sometimes I'd catch Mum sneering at Rosa as she played with her toys. Mum spent more and more time at church. There was cleaning to do, bake sales to organise, studies to run. When she actually talked to us, she spoke only of Jesus and Pastor Drew.

Rosa was left to me. I was a parent at eleven. I didn't mind. We'd read stories and eat noodles in front of the TV until the adults got home and we were sent to bed.

It was Rosa's last day of school before the summer holidays. She woke me up, all excited about the school trip to the swimming pool. She bounced on my bed, singing 'Henry, Henry, Henry, Henry' until I opened my eyes. She laughed milky breath over my face. She ran for the door, opened it, swayed for a second on the threshold and threw up in the hallway.

'Oh no.' She wiped her mouth, lowered herself to the floor and curled in a ball. 'Henry, why's the room spinning?'

I knelt beside her, stroked her hair and called for Mum. Mum picked pieces of carrot from the carpet with un-covered hands, muttering prayers under her breath, like she did when she was angry.

'You'll have to take her to the doctor's,' she said, when she ran out of prayers.

'Why me?'

'Because, I'm busy. Drew is picking me up in half an hour for the conference in the city. We've been planning it for months. I can't let him down.'

'But, I'm not old enough to take her to the doctor's by myself. You have to come.'

'I can't.' She sighed, chewed her lip. 'I'll get your father.' She rose, collected the bowl of carrot chunks and left. Rosa asked if that meant she couldn't go on the trip. I said it did. She sniffed and wiped her nose on my pajama sleeves. We rode to the GP in silence, Rosa's head in my lap and Cold Chisel rattling out of the ute stereo. My father drove recklessly. Rosa threw up on my shoes.

We crunched up the path to the doctor. Rosa ran up to our father, sucking her fingers, grabbing his hand, leaning against his leg for support. He stopped. His back stiffened, his other hand shook. He jerked away, turned to me with wide eyes.

'You'll take care of this?' He threw the Medicare card at me and hurried off to the corner shop. I took Rosa's hand, and led her to the steps. We waited for him. I didn't know if he'd come back, but there was nothing else we could do. When he did, he followed us sheepishly inside.

The doctor said it was just an ear infection. Rosa cried when he said she couldn't go swimming for half the summer.

'Not even when it's real hot?' she asked, hopeful.

'Not even then. Sorry.' He handed her a lollipop and me a prescription for antibiotics.

On the ride home, Rosa made me promise not to go swimming without her.

That summer we sat inside and planned adventures in my atlas.

A week after my sixteenth birthday, I walked home from footy training with the last embers of sun at my back. I passed the chapel and peeked in the windows to see if Mum had finished her prayer meeting yet. It was very still inside. The lights were off, everything looked cold. I wiped mud from my knees and continued home.

I stumbled through the front door of our house and

called to Mum. I asked what time tea would be, I was starving. Nothing. I threw my footy gear on the bed, sending flakes of mud across the blankets. 'Mum.' I went to the kitchen. It was dark and cold, like the church. 'Mum?'

'She's not here,' called my father from the back porch. I went out to meet him. He had an empty bottle in his fingertips. I asked where she was. He just said, gone.

'What, like to the shops or something?' I asked. He said no, just gone, away, for good. 'What?' was all I could manage.

'Look, she's nicked off with that fucking pastor.' He stared into the yard.

The words hit me hard in the back and rippled through my lungs, like a tackle on the footy field. I stood silent for a moment. She wouldn't leave us here, alone, with him, would she?

'But she's coming back for Rosa and me, right?'

'No. No, you're stuck with me.'

'I didn't mean—'

'Doesn't matter.' He shook his bottle, heard it was empty and lobbed it into the backyard. I looked back into the creaking house.

'Where's Rosa?' I asked.

'Asleep in my room. She came home all excited with this painting she wanted to show your mother. Ran around the house until she tuckered herself out and climbed into my bed.' He pushed hair from his face and rubbed his temples. 'She doesn't know. I thought...I thought you should tell her.'

'Yeah.'

He pinched his nose and his mouth twisted like it did on the stump years ago.

I went inside and switched the kettle on. Tea always helped me organise my thoughts. A trick I'd picked up from my English nan. The whistling kettle couldn't drown out the creaking walls or the sobs of my father. My hands trembled as I yanked on the teabags.

I made two cups – strong, with milk and one sugar – and sat beside my father on the porch.

'Here.' I handed him a cup. I didn't even know if he liked tea. He looked at the cup and then at me. His mouth untwisted.

'Thanks.' He held the cup like a foreign object until he saw how I cradled mine to warm my fingers and did the same. He looked tired, broken, child-like. I thought of Rosa asleep in the other room.

We watched the light disappear and reappear with the popping streetlights.

LONG LEGS

Maja Hagen Torjussen

She sits on the bench in front of the plastic table, one leg dangling. Her shaggy, brown-blonde hair is a fuzzy palm on top of her head. Her shoulders shake as laughter falls out from between her white teeth. I can see how her skin wrinkles on her nose and under her eyes. Slander, those long, laughing wrinkles. I see her dark red lipstick, the blue nail polish, the fingers on her right hand, a thin grip on the stem of her wine glass. She sits among the others; there aren't many left.

The bar is closed, but we keep on with our drinks, our noise. Me and my friends and she who came here to sit with them: to talk, and laugh with them. She doesn't know them. That Live's boyfriend – the one with the purple scar under his left eye – died two years ago. He used to bite his nails. She doesn't know Andrea has her own studio, but never sold a single painting. She gives them away for free.

Those long legs belong to me. She stands so firmly, never needing me to pet her cheek. She always says everything's great if I ask her how she's doing. Then she smiles so wide I can see her red tongue, staring at the ceil-ing, counting her fingers to make sure they're all still there. She tells me stories about her day: something strange happened, she says. Something strange always happens. Or maybe she's just a skilled storyteller, making trivialities unique.

It means something that she's still by my side; I'm enough for her, too. I assume the length of my hair suits her. Maybe she likes how I open the door in my underwear when she comes to visit. I prefer her staying at my place. I don't like the thought of her being alone at hers, smoking, reading. It's so tiny there, the single bed, the desk. She doesn't even have a cupboard for her clothes; they're all on the floor. I can see what she's doing and where she's going when she stays at mine.

I give her the rest of my cigarette. She rarely wants a whole one on nights out, but she smokes twenty a day inside the flat. She's special, my Long Legs. Assertive. Clever, I can tell by her silences. She tells me to fuck off when she wants to, especially when I'm inside her. And, she's mysterious. She told me once: the day before I met you, I was sick. I read a novel all day, had no time to eat, I couldn't go to the bathroom 'cause there was something on the walls in there, made my guts twist. I wet my pants, she said. She never tells me all her secrets, or explains herself. They're hidden in her eyes. I see them, but I can't read them. She gives me a tiny bit of herself, as if she doesn't really need me, but here she is, sitting amongst my friends, one finger playing with the hair tucked behind her ear. The other hand is a fist on her lap. Her back is straight, she looks *feminine*. My friends stare at her shoes, her chest, the neckline on her overalls cut down to her navel. They admire her vulgarity, her humour and intelligence. I can see her covering her flaws with long sentences and laughter, like a con artist. Live looks awkward, in comparison, they all do. Like they chose the wrong clothes, and she doesn't even have to try to be right. She never talks about the way I dress: black hoodie, tangled hair. There are holes in the hood, she's never commented on it.

I'm starting to feel wasted. I switch to a different record then take the headset off, put it on the table in front of me. It falls to the floor. I leave the disc spinning, walk past her hot legs, into the toilet. I take a piss, dribble on the toilet seat, and don't bother to wipe it up. I reach down my sock for a little plastic bag, take a card from my back pocket, slam down the toilet cap, pour a little powder on it, gather a nice little stripe on the white lid. I roll a fifty into a tube, and sniff it up. Heading back out I feel even better. Clearer now. And oh, this track. Does she know it's for her, this reggae jazz?

Long Legs dances, spinning Live under her arm. They press their hips against each other. I watch the chemistry between them, in their synchronised rhythm. I like them both, simultaneously, as well as separately. Long Legs' long legs are more flexible now, like rubber. Her hair is messy, as if she's been electro-shocked. Her mascara has stained her face, as if she's been crying. She's sweating on her forehead and her upper lip. Then abruptly, she turns, heading outside for a cigarette. She doesn't ask anyone to join her. Live's still dancing. She's rougher, less feminine. She watches me as she dances, and I change the song for her.

Long Legs comes back and leans over the mixing desk. I can see a bit of her dark brown nipple. She fixes her hair.

I'm going home, she says. Give me your keys.

I'm disappointed, but I shrug and nod. I tell her to leave the keys under the doormat for me. She kisses my cheek, and disappears through the door. The people she's left behind are distant background details. I can only see Live, Live who stays. Long Legs who trusts me to stay. I shouldn't feel rejected. She's heading home to my bed. She's waiting for me.

Live's dancing. I drink on. I sniff coke straight from the mixing desk then share some with her. She snorts it from the crotch of my jeans. Long Legs is sleeping in my bed, waiting for me to come and hold her. She needs that, I know, me holding her.

My cheek is sweaty from the velvet couch. There's a low coffee table in front of me. My arm is asleep; I let it fall to the floor and dangle my fingertips to get the blood circulating again. I wonder what time it is. The head of a moose hangs on the wall opposite. The furniture is carved, dark wood. It smells of old cabin, spilt alcohol and cigarettes. My tongue tastes like metal. Burnt-out joints are spread on the tables, some needles. A painting, and oil colours. My mobile's flashing on the table. I'm naked. I have three missed calls. Long Legs. She should have been here, all the fun she missed out on.

I yell for Geir, and ask him when he's getting out of here. It's too far to walk. The mobile rings again. Where the hell are you, Long Legs says. I tell her I'm with Geir, and why does she sound so grouchy? I don't recognise that voice; besides, she's the one who left. She hangs up. My head aches. I turn over and go back to sleep.

When I wake up again, I find dried blood on my inner thigh, dead skin under my fingernails. I meet Live in the hallway, she sees me naked, and she sees the blood. She takes toilet paper from a drawer, drips water on it from the sink. She wipes my legs, pushing the paper against my wounds, sitting on her knees, like a beggar. She watches my penis thicken, harden. She doesn't stop staring until it's completely hard. She looks up, into my eyes, and begins to blow me, holding my gaze. Don't fucking look away, I tell her. My phone's ringing. I'm about to come, I whisper, I'm coming, I'm coming, I'm coming.

Long Legs texts me. She says she's leaving, taking a plane, moving today, she's done, and she's sick of my face. I don't understand why she's changed. I tell her to get her act together, but she won't calm down, so I say I don't give a shit where she goes. I tell her she's a prop, a wagging dog's tail. She hangs up again.

We leave Geir's, and head off for Indian food. In the restaurant, the sofa covers are red velvet; the walls are painted red and gold. Live's sitting next to me, Geir and Andreas sit opposite. Live keeps her hand on my thigh underneath the table, rubbing it up and down. She's beautiful: the zipper on the sleeves of her leather jacket, her blonde dreadlocks and the skinny ring in her nose that she fingers while ordering four beers. Geir tells us about when he was in Cambodia and got chased by wild dogs; he waves his hands, talking. People in the restaurant stare as we laugh. I suppose we're quite loud. Geir tells us how he ran out of his own shoes. I cannot stop laughing. Andreas tells us about mushrooms and where to look for them. Big fields, he says, vast meadows full of green grass. If you see pine trees, you can just forget it, he says. Live nods her head eagerly. She smiles at me, I smile back. Long Legs won't leave me, I think. Where would she go? There's no one else who sees her the way I do. Large meadows and birch trees, says Andreas. I think about large meadows and birch trees, a distant chaffinch singing in the background. Long Legs standing there, all alone, her long hair waving in the breeze. I touch her shoulder, trying to make contact in some way. But she turns her back on me, disappearing among the birch trees. The chaffinch follows her, and I'm left alone.

My head aches. Geir and Andreas keep going on about the mushrooms. Live has stopped laughing. There's a coldness between us now. Her hand is no longer on my thigh. I tell them I'm not feeling very well, that it's time for me to go.

My feet are freezing as I walk. The two blocks seem long. The buildings around me are stiff and metallic. The keys aren't under the mat. I knock on my neighbour's window, and a face with red cheeks pokes through the violet curtains. I point at the lock. She lets me in.

I walk into my apartment. Long Legs' stuff's still there. I want to tell her about all the fun I had, but when I sneak my head through the bedroom door, she's asleep. She looks so peaceful, so kind and warm. A different person from the one I spoke to on the phone. Then my eyes adjust to the dim light in the room, and I realise what she's been doing all night. The bedroom walls are covered with pages and pages of newspaper. I stare. She's drawn rings around words, and lines out of the rings, like a fucking map. A web. Where the hell did she get the newspapers? Her notebook lies open on the floor, coffee stained. There's a half-empty bottle of gin beside the ashtray.

I sit down on the bed and say her name. I want to do

her good, more than she would ever expect from me. She squirms onto her back and opens her eyes. She's sweaty, and her makeup is all over her face. Hi, she says. Feeling better, I ask her. Yes, she replies, but you could've sent a message. I'm so tired of this. I'm glad you didn't come home earlier, I was so angry. I will not spend my time waiting on you. I lose my time, it becomes yours. I can't, she says. Ssh, I say. I stroke her cheek, kiss her forehead, curl up beside her, and fold my arms around her waist. Is it better now, I ask. Yes, she replies. Let's forget about it, she says, and tightens my arms around her. She pulls her steady, long model legs up to her belly. Slowly, I tangle my fingers in her hair. Must do it slowly, carefully, try not to stir her new calm. You know how happy I am now, I tell her. She strokes my hand.

She loves me. I know she does.

Above our heads, the newspaper stirs, like her hair.

MOTHER'S DAY

Francoise Macaly

I like to sit at the table my husband made before I clean my kitchen. I leave cleaning the table until last, like the joy of reading a book before bed. It was Pascal who taught me how to clean – my husband wasn't good for much, but he knew how to carve wood and keep tidy.

Keep everything clean so nobody knows nothing, he'd say.

Whenever Pascal came home from work, he'd go straight upstairs to smoke, leaving me in the kitchen until the dinner was done. Not even a simple hello. He only ever walked through the front door and into the kitchen, two times. The first was to tell me he couldn't sell that table he'd made. It was the size of the whole room and the swirls in the wood reminded me of the marble cakes I baked after church. I was eight months pregnant with Brandon and Errol had just started play school. We kept the table in the kitchen and I was glad. I cleaned it every day, knowing that Brandon would be born on it. Having Errol had taught me that Mauritian hospitals were expensive and not as clean as my table at home.

The second time my husband came home and walked straight into the kitchen was to tell me something I'd known for years. He slammed both doors behind him and stood against the table, puffing on his cigarette. I'd just put the boys to bed and come down for a glass of water. I would've poured one for him too, but his hand was around a bottleneck. He followed me to the sink and stubbed out the cigarette on the cupboard above our heads. He began to inch forward, pushing me, squashing me, muttering he loved me, but all I could hear was the alcohol sloshing around in the bottle, like the water in my belly.

'The business is going buss,' he whispered. He rested his head in the cave of my neck and kissed me. When we were young I would've kissed him back and held his hand, but these days his hands were full of cigarettes and bottles. He pressed the glass bottle against my leg and I tried not to flinch. He sighed into my hair, then sat down at the table.

I didn't move. I faced the sink and kept my eyes on the tap. I could feel him staring at me, at my legs, at my nightie. Just as I rested my glass in the sink and turned to leave, the drink kicked in. He dropped his bottle and flew at me. His body knocked into mine, bashing my head against the cupboard. He grabbed me by my nightie and pushed me down on to the table. He hit me so hard, his rings bruised my skin. I don't know how long we were there for, but when he bashed my head against the table and I started to bleed, he stopped.

I slept there, in the middle of that table, for the whole night, like I did when I had Brandon. I lay on my front and let the coolness of the wood soothe my swollen body. When morning came, I picked myself up and tidied the blood and shattered glass, before the boys woke up.

A few weeks later, Pascal left and didn't say goodbye. I picked up my babies and we moved into my mother's house across town. She looked after the boys while I worked, and when I'd saved enough for a ticket to England, I sat my children down one night before dinner.

'I'm sorry Daddy has gone,' I said. I held Errol's hand and let Brandon suck on one of my fingers. 'But Mammy is moving to England soon and Grandma is going to look after you until I can bring you over too.'

Errol refused to eat his dinner that evening; he cried all night and every night until the day I left. My first night in England was awful. I remember thinking I would rather sleep with my weeping son than cry alone in an empty flat. Money was slow for the first two months. I couldn't afford to pay for my babies' tickets after the first year, but I could manage the money to bring my table over. Some might think it selfish, but it was the only thing I had to help me cope. For five years I cooked, cleaned, worked and cried over my table, singing my promise to my boys like a Psalm.

The rice had finished steaming when I heard Errol's car outside. His Sega music blared out of his car window and I could hear Brandon singing along like a mad fool all the way to the front door. I put the lid on the rice as Brandon put his key in the door.

'Happy Mother's Day!'

Brandon marched into the kitchen and hugged me. He was holding a bunch of pink carnations and a yellow envelope. I don't think I'll ever get used to resting my head on his chest when he hugs me. I don't think any mother gets used to their children growing taller than them.

Errol closed the front door behind him. He walked over and kissed my forehead then showed me the blue plastic bag hanging from his wrist. He fished around the bottom of it and smiled as he pulled out a tiny chilli pepper. 'I got a couple of these to put in the food, Mammy. Make you suck in air good.'

Brandon put the flowers in a vase and rested my Mother's Day card in front. I hugged my two boys, my arms straining to fit around them both, and enjoyed the carnations, glowing against the dark wood.

'Get the playing cards, Brandon,' Errol said. He sat down at the head of the table. 'You playing Mammy?' Nothing's changed since they arrived in England, all those years ago. We have to find the playing cards before anything else. I carried my chopping board and knife over to the table, along with Errol's bag of groceries. Brandon dealt us each a hand, the cards sliding underneath my chopping board each time they flew across the table. He put the deck down by the vase and turned the top card over.

'Queen of hearts.' He winked at me.

'You smell these flowers, Mammy?' Errol asked. He put down a king of hearts; I put down my knife and leaned over to smell the flowers. 'Brandon said they smell like that flower bush in the garden back home, the one next to the tree where the castor apples fell.' Their faces lit up.

'The amount of time we spent under that tree trying to catch those apples,' Brandon said. 'And nobody made them apple pies like you, Mum.' I nodded and picked up my cards. The boys grinned at each other like Cheshire cats.

Brandon put down an eight of hearts, which meant I missed my next turn.

'Them pies were good,' I said. When I was a little girl, I loved apples. I fell in love with Pascal the day he told me I was the apple of his eye. When he started beating me, and my skin bruised like apple peel, I stopped eating them and started to cook with them instead. I don't mind England being cold. I like being able to add layers to keep warm, more than not being able to take them off. I'd rub them castor apple peels on my skin to soothe the burning. Like aloe vera. I peeled so many apples, it seemed foolish not to dash them into a pie for the boys.

'I wonder why those castor apples don't grow here,' Brandon said.

'Because the sun don't know how to stay out of the cloud's way,' Errol laughed, shuffling his cards. 'Bit like you, Mammy. You'd only make them pies after you and Daddy fight. You should have stayed out his way. Maybe he run off because you make too much pie.'

The boys laughed, but I didn't find anything funny. I carried on chopping.

Brandon sucked in his breath as Errol played his turn. When I looked up, there was a two of hearts on top of the deck. Errol played like his dad: he'd kick off the game and then sit back to watch the next player suffer. Brandon rushed through his cards, hoping to find some way to win. Errol slid the deck closer to Brandon, eager for him to pick up, but Brandon smacked down a triumphant two of clubs. They laughed and turned to me, waiting. I placed my two of diamonds on the deck. Errol stopped laughing and sighed. 'I wish I could've packed some of those apples in my case,' Brandon said. 'And some sunshine too.' 'That sun was too hot sometimes,' Errol spoke from behind his cards. 'Remember the day we left for Grandma's, Mammy said, cover your ears to keep them from burning? The neighbours were picking mangoes and pointing at us like they'd never seen people walking in the sun before. Their shoulders bounced and their foreheads rippled like water. People here would think we mad, too.'

'I don't remember that,' said Brandon.

'You were a baby,' said Errol. He grabbed the deck and counted out six cards for himself.

I remembered that morning. I'd dreaded walking through town. I didn't want people to see me, carrying a bag full of food and clothes on my back. I could hear them muttering from their front gardens as Brandon slept in a sling around my chest. They cursed me for making Errol hold the hem of my dress when he got too tired to cover his ears. I didn't want him to hear the neighbours whisper me a slut for leaving my husband. Being beat was bad, but there was no apple peel to soothe shame.

'Sometimes I wonder if Mauritius has changed,' Brandon said. 'Do you think everyone lives in the same place?'

'I want to know who's living in our house,' Errol said.

'Can you imagine if Daddy had moved back in?' Brandon said. 'Or maybe he's made a new house with another table like this.' My eyes started to prickle, so I stopped chopping and rested my knife on the blue bag. 'Wouldn't you'd love to go back, Mum?' He leaned to the left so he could see me, past the vase. 'Imagine if you went back for a visit and it wasn't as bad as you think?'

Errol glanced at me. 'She'd probably move back,' he said, pulling a card from his hand. 'Then we'd have to wait another five years before we were invited. She'd send this rotten table over, though.' He leaned across the table and whacked down a black jack of spades. The vase wobbled and my Mother's Day card fell down. I wiped my eyes on my sleeve and tried to hide my face. I carried my knife and chopping board over to the counter.

'You know Mammy, if you cut the onions and suck on a spoon you won't cry,' Errol said.

'No, if you wash the onions in cold water, *then* you won't cry,' Brandon said.

'I'm cutting tomatoes,' I said.

The boys fell silent. Brandon put his cards down. Neither one of them looked at me, but they knew I was staring at them. I marched over to the table, pulled out my red jack from the rest of my cards, and slammed it down on top of the pile. My voice wobbled like the vase, but I made sure it didn't fall like my card. 'Your father *beat* me. He beat me, he beat me, he beat me.'

They stared at my red jack, their faces still and silent.

We didn't play another game for a while. I put some onions into the biryani, along with the tomatoes. I even added some of the chillies Errol bought. I'm glad I can put a few chillies in the food, now that the boys have grown up and can handle the heat.

I served the food. Brandon shuffled the cards and the sound cooled the air. I kissed them both on the tops of their heads.

After dinner, we played another hand and sucked in air all night to cool our mouths. I think I cooked with too many onions, because our eyes watered around the dinner table. But the more you cook with them, the less they sting.

LUNAM

Cleo Wreford

The tavern was crowded, all the men crammed in and stinking of the day's work. They didn't pay her any heed. They never did, although she'd soon be of age to marry. She didn't know what was worse: that they ignored her, or that she was glad of it.

It was even louder in the tavern than usual. The last full moon of the farming year was here and the birds had already flown south, leaving the mornings quiet. Her father was in his usual corner, foam clinging to his beard as he laughed and joked with the men about him. She knew he'd seen her, but she was made to wait, as usual, fiddling with the beads about her neck. This was not a place for good women; the tiny hairs on the back of her neck prickled with every wave of laughter or body shouldering past her.

Her sixteenth birthday was but a week away, and with it would come suitors. The other girls giggled and whispered about which man they'd like to wed, but Ursa dreaded the prospect. She was taller than most, built too solidly for pretty dresses and airs and graces. It was just her and her father. He worked the fields, and Ursa did the work of a son and daughter, her hands roughened from chopping wood and her skin dark from the sun. If she'd had a brother, one that loved her, maybe life would have been easier. She wouldn't have had to marry; he could inherit everything and let her be.

Wed the girl and get the farm once her father died. That was incentive, enough, she knew. Men had married for far less, wooed girls far more ugly. But she didn't want to be trapped, especially with someone who didn't care about her, nor bear children for someone cold.

'Why are you here?'

Her father's words were half-lost in the hubbub, but she knew exactly what he was saying. This was their daily routine. She'd come to fetch him, and he'd tell her to go, then complain when he wobbled home drunk to cold supper.

'Your food. It's ready.'

'Well I'm not ready to go, stupid girl. Cook later, like I've told you to!'

More laughter.

He'd complain no matter what she did. If she cooked late, he came home early. If she cooked early, he came home late. Keeping him waiting brought far worse temper than cold food ever had. When he was drunk, all he wanted was to eat, then sleep; he would forget her sins come the morning. Sober, he was far more inclined to punish her for insolence.

Ursa turned away, wriggling past a group of tuneless singers, and out into the night. The road was gloomy but that was no trouble for her. She walked it every evening. When she got back she'd sit and repair clothes or shoes until her father came home. There was no sense in going to sleep and being awoken, having to rekindle the fire to heat up his missed meal, to stumble outside in her nightgown to gather wood from the log-pile. Still, tonight the nerves from the tavern seemed to follow her into the cloud-dimmed moonlight. She was aware of everything, stopping to gaze about her, troubled by what, she knew not. It was as if she was being watched; the thought of long jaws filled with spittle and teeth making her skin constrict about her sides and shoulders. What ailed her? There were no wolves in these parts, not this time of year. In winter her father hunted them, but for the next few weeks they'd be off, chasing the vast deer herds to the north. She'd never seen a live wolf. Only the carcasses skinned and pink and splotched with blood. The sight made her ill. Her father had wolf pelts on his bed, but Ursa's blankets were wool. She couldn't imagine sleeping under something that had died for her pleasure.

A fox screamed, out in the deep woods. It sounded almost human.

She began moving again, the rustling of the trees seeming to follow her as she picked up speed. She'd not been scared going home since she was a child, but this strange discomfort felt more real than the monsters she'd imagined when she was small. Her necklace bounced against her chest, the tangle of blue beads smacking hard enough to hurt. Before she knew herself, she was running, her calves burning with the effort and her breath so loud she could no longer hear the swoosh-hiss of the trees.

Something huge and grey and furry arced over the path, inches from her face, and she sprawled into the dirt. With no time to catch herself, she was winded, one cheek flat in the earth, her arms prickling. She'd likely have some bruises tomorrow. Grazes were certain. Her breasts hurt. She lay, still shocked at the impact of her body against the earth.

The fox called again. Ursa lay, shivering. Her palms were beginning to regain the feeling that had been knocked out of them, the prickling turning into a sharp sting. There were smooth, small somethings beneath her fingers, and she closed her fist on them as she scrambled to her feet. The road was empty, the woods quiet about her. The sense of being watched had gone, but there was enough memory of it to set her limping onward.

She clutched the small things until she got home, leaving them on the table to light a fire, wash her scraped face and hands, change into her nightgown. In the tawny light she could see them properly. Nine blue beads, carved with the phases of the moon, now loose and jumbled. She had lost most of them.

She gathered them into her hands and sat before the fire. The necklace had belonged to her mother; she had imagined the grey beast and for fear, lost the most precious thing she owned. She twisted a bead between two of her nails, squeezed too hard and send it spinning across the floor, in the same moment the door opened.

The smell of ale preceded him, as always, but this was not her father's usual attempt to be quiet. She stayed still, staring at him. He bent, picking up the bead, examining it. Emotions rippled on his face. Anger; fear?

'Father, I –'

He dropped it and moved toward her, seizing her shoulder. The beads spilt across the floor, two crackling inside the fire, but he ignored them. He punched her. His hand was calloused, leather-skinned; the blow made the edges of her vision bloom black.

When she surfaced again, the house smelled like meat. She knew he was dead before she saw his body on the floor, his throat shredded. She'd done it, after all, although it was not her. No; it was both her and not-her, something that had lain small in her for these years. She turned to the door, leaving her stained nightgown on the floor behind her. The blood on her collarbone smelled sweet.

The night was lazy now, the rustle of the leaves like an ocean – and there, a call, a howl streaming skywards. Ursa surged forward, spine pliant, landing on her grey paws.

Teeth.

She ran toward the moon.

SCREAMS & SILENCES
[POETRY SEQUENCE RESPONDING TO THE WORK OF EDVARD MUNCH]

Marita Algroy

Kiss By The Window (1)

this is a blouse blues
this is a beloved wife
this is a sleazy bastard
this is a hotel room, booked for one
this is a bereavement of dignity
this is a blessed moment
this is a bloody memory
this is a melting pot, so busty!
this is a widow's wish
this is window bliss
this is a warm spot
this is damned hot
this is a Monday evening (December)
this is that night (remember?)
this is a painting of three people (several imagined: sleeping,
working, masturbating behind closed doors)
this is an examined moment
this is a repetition of history (it is done before)
this is to be repeated (you never finish anything, Munch)

Kiss By The Window (2)

he strokes her diagonally (outside the painting)
from the knee up we are all lovers hovering in
the street: Leila has lost her house keys
four entries to enlightenment in this blues

Amor And Psyche

before language
your skin is a rainbow

Puberty

the shadow when the shadow the shadow behind you
is behind you & heavy hips you have heavy hips & heaving
have been & have coming
alone in the room you cross your arms & you are & you are
& you are but your shadow your shadow of hips is too heavy

Red Virginia Creeper

there is yellow in the white there are
naked trees there are white fences guarding
gardens there is a road leading to the house
in which a naked woman cries there is
a man leaving wide-eyed no one is laughing
not even a bark from that damned dog next door

Evening On Karl Johan

river running ravaged faces
the roofs are crucial not as
round as usual cut the sky
as a hole the hole runs
through their eyes fill the
empty canvas with something
Emptier!

The Murderess

Munch painted the room as if it was a garden
spring in a garden all is sun & green grass
great day she combed her hair this morning happy
put on the low cut dress it is spring & desire
bring cake! bring cake & the cake knife she is oh!
so happy to see him bleeding in bed that bastard
stand by the plant and smile please as Edward pleases

Scream (1)

the   sky   bursts

        this   moment

at   the   bridge

                    broken

              open &

               hollow your

           mouth & words

       & thought & soul

            o!

Scream (2)

yeah that screamin' geezer don't worry
he was schizophrenic or somthin'

HAPPY HOUR

Jamie Hubner

I stood at the lights, waiting for the red man to turn green, night air trickling down my throat and making me cough. I sounded like a radiator rattling back to life. Every time I came to Westbourne Park, it seemed like I saw the same people over and over again. That short, ginger-haired man in a green shooting jacket; that dark-haired woman, gold watch and leggings a couple of sizes too small, stretched so tight they were see-through; the same two pudgy girls talking louder than the oncoming traffic, still wearing the same tan-strapped boots and too much make-up in strange shades of pink and aqua blue. It was as if the neighbourhood was populated by the same two hundred people, all extras in my life. They worked bad shifts and hid catering vans on a side street maybe, just out of my view.

I was nervous, meeting my date for the evening. Dating isn't English; it's American. It's been blown up like a balloon, until it's so close you lose all perspective, like Halloween. I couldn't remember my date's face. We'd met and exchanged numbers at a Camden bar, both dragged in by friends. I was five minutes late and all I could remember was that she was brunette.

I crossed the road and headed toward the restaurant. I'd chosen the place in a moment of ear-aching panic after my text message request for a date was accepted – the first faux-American bar I knew within one bus journey. I wondered if she'd get the joke. Probably not.

I walked into the bar and looked at the posters of up-coming events and NFL Sunday hot wing deals that lined the walls. My eyes began to water. I'd left my glasses at home, thinking I'd look cooler without them, but it'd been a bad idea. I wasn't blind, but I didn't recognise anybody. Couples and groups sat and talked, their tables full of half-eaten burgers and fries, served in little plastic baskets. In the corner, a brunette in a lime-green leather booth sat and stared at a game of tennis between two girls with unpronounceable names, playing on a wall mounted television.

I caught her eye and she smiled; a little too widely, I thought. She waved.

I sat down opposite the brunette, removed my coat, and began to navigate the first-conversation assault course. There was a rectangular mirror behind her head, in a faded, spray-painted gold frame. I stared into the mirror and nodded too often. I didn't look like myself. The brunette explained her technique for buying Christmas presents. Bar staff put tea-lights in jam jars on tables. The kitchen door opened and closed, filling the bar with the smell of frying burgers and oil. The opening chords of *Lola* played through the speaker above my head and cut through our conversation. I slumped back in my seat and wondered why some of my favourite songs were about transvestites. My attention switched back to the mirror behind the brunette.

There she was, or rather, her reflection. She was sitting at the end of the bar.

Jayne.

I could only see her from the back, but her hair was that same dirty straw shade. I turned around and squinted at the girl who might have been Jayne across the crowded bar. Perhaps it was just a trick of my addled mind.

She was sitting on a stool that was too tall to be practical. Her feet reached only halfway to the floor; one shoelace was loose and dangling. She was drinking something red through a straw. We had decided to break up a few months after I moved to London. We lived at opposite ends of the country and the train journeys to see each other when we had time off work became less frequent and eventually stopped altogether. We both felt like we'd already broken up. So we left it at that.

The brunette asked if I was okay. I said I was fine and turned back to show her she had my attention. As she carried on speaking, I felt the ligaments in my neck push against the top button of my shirt as I strained to get a view of the blonde. I squinted, but she wouldn't come into focus.

I told the brunette I was going to powder my nose, wincing at my choice of phrase. I snaked my way past tables toward the gent's. I was close enough to see the blonde girl's black roots. Some loose strands of hair were stuck to the bobbles on the back of her jumper. Jayne threw out clothes the second they went bobbly. I got to within touching distance of maybe-Jayne, when a crowd of men wearing easy-iron suits crowded the bar around her, knocking me backwards. I fell into a table full of drinks, apologised to the two women sitting there glaring at me, and wriggled around the suited men to the gent's, still none the wiser.

A man was standing at the urinal, leaning the palms of both hands on the wall, above posters about prostate cancer awareness. The only cubicle had a laminated Out Of Order sign, attached with blue tack. I moved toward the urinal, my trainers sticking a little on the tiled floor, and unzipped. I didn't need to go. The man beside me made more noise than is acceptable at a urinal – groans of bladder emptying pleasure – then zipped up and left without washing his hands.

I looked down at the day-old urinal cake eroding in the basin. Why would Jayne be in London? I didn't want Jayne to be in London.

I let out the breath I'd held in since I approached the urinal, zipped up, and washed my hands anyway. I had to dry my hands on my jeans; the wall-mounted hand-dryer was yellowing like a smoker's tooth, and as much use as an ant breathing on me. I'd get a good look at maybe-Jayne going back. Once I knew it wasn't her I could relax and enjoy my date. The brunette was pleasant enough: I needed to be more charming. I needed to get it together. I pulled open the door, letting it swing back on its hinges and make a dull thud against the wall.

The suited men were still a buffer between me and maybe-Jayne. I looked through the gaps at the crowded bar as I walked back to my booth. She was sitting with the man who hadn't washed his hands, both elevated on those ridiculous bar stools, her face still turned away. I watched him run his pissy left hand along the outline of her jeans pocket.

The brunette waved and smiled; I couldn't stand here, staring at another woman.

I got back to the lime booth and wiped beads of sweat from my top lip. The smell of burgers and frying stuck to me. The brunette told me how much she enjoyed tennis, but didn't get to play as often as she liked; then about her office job somewhere near King's Cross, and how it made her depressed. I shifted in my seat, the fake leather stuck to me. My eyes darted between the mirror and the brunette, between maybe-probably-not-but-almost-surely-Jayne and the unhygienic man. I told the brunette even Picasso got the blues, and that it had been one of his more successful periods. She frowned and said something I didn't hear. I itched all over. I watched the man put his hands all over probably-Jayne, reaching one into her hair and turning her face toward him. I strained my neck to get a clear view, but things were too fuzzy to be sure. He whispered in her ear. I checked the smell of my shirt – burgers and anti-perspirant. The brunette asked me a question, but I felt as if someone had dunked me under at the swimming baths.

The man with pissy hands leaned in to kiss Jayne.

I got to my feet, banging my kneecap on the underside of the table. I moved through the crowded bar, knocking over people and drinks. They were kissing and I didn't know what I'd do when I got there, until I was finally close enough and my hands were on his shoulders, pulling him away from her kiss, so she could finally turn around and see me, too.

The blonde girl had a mole near her eyebrow, half obscured by her puzzled frown. Her tongue was stained red from her drink. She said something. I stared at her nose piercings and thought about how much Jayne would disapprove.

Before I could say a word I felt the man's right hand, wet with what I hoped was sweat, hit the bridge of my nose and right cheek. The punch sounded like somebody stamped on Rice Krispies. I felt my nose fill with blood and the cold floor tiles against my skin when I hit the floor. Music played but I didn't recognise the song. The smell of burgers disappeared. Blood filled my mouth; I felt it seep into the crack in my filling and the gaps in my teeth. By the time I sat up, they were gone.

I walked back to my empty corner booth, feeling the blood flake off my top lip when I moved my mouth. I took a sip from the drink the brunette had left behind. The glass had a red stain on the rim – from my nose, or her lipstick, I couldn't tell. I looked into the mirror. I saw myself, bloodstained, and laughed at the reflection. A waitress appeared and asked me to leave. I couldn't reply; I couldn't catch my breath. A bouncer appeared and grabbed the back of my shirt collar to force me out of the booth. I dragged my feet and watched a button pop off my shirt and roll around on the floor tiles. I looked up at the television and saw Caroline Wozniacki serve a second fault. The bouncer used most of my body to shove open the door and then pushed me so I fell into the street. I lay on my back on the pavement and held my elbow up so I could see it in the streetlight. My shirt was torn. My elbow had burst open. It hurt like hell. I needed to speak to Jayne. I needed to listen to her laugh when I told her about my night. I reached into my back pocket for my phone. When I pulled it out, the screen was shattered. I dragged myself up off the pavement and set off home.

It was only a bus ride away.

721ST day of falling

Audrey Jean

t'was made of lonely star
& some shadows from the heavens
below, forever in motion—
      wondering how something in decay
      could be so maddeningly, beautifully
      alive
                              /yet

           ·

i noticed his eyes in quiet wonder
                     on the 13th day
i followed them there & back /
human eyes—unlike his other half

           ·

it all drifted apart, apart
           from each other
     /in uncharted territory
                /terrifying spacefield
i tried to keep it together
                    on the 36th day

           ·

it's like a shard of laughter
           wedged in his throat & refused to let go
             /lodging most comfortably it showed all the way

up his eyes
& i followed suit, core melting
(i tried to splint some more
from the 51st day on)

.

/i started to understand
on the 92nd day

.

i packed my sorrows and left town—
i wondered about the way
things should be
& above, the sky told me to stay
inside (washed away
by dark matter & tempests of dust— navigating the stars
with her
him
& them)
/only that could (ever) make us free

.

/127th day in, already done for

.

what didya say?
him?
/four levels down, i confirmed

.

a few intakes of conditioned

(living) atmosphere
and the quiet hum of static,
unforgiving, laying it
bare

.

they say red & green complete each other
/gold & blue, too?
i wonder—

.

/yes, they do
in battle, in bed— i want both, mind you

.

234th day in & i still dream of things—
the pale blue light of a star
resonating his own dust
/eyes, human eyes
closed for once
the warm aura of his
halfness /
the shatter of asteroids
dragged out of his throat— lungs burning

.

/the mind, the touch

.

he lost it in front of me—
i can only make out words, a salute

/a farewell & half-confession
before everything fades out

.

no light
on the 317th day

.

he dies in front of me now
(all night, most nights) or it's me
having trouble with blackholes-filled nightmares—
again & again (& again)
/event horizon disquieting,
returning my stare

.

sometimes, he
just leaves
/into the void, the void creeping again, calling
me— my mind & bones & heart (dripping black)

.

no light
on the 342nd day

.

no light
on the 343rd day

.

i warm my flesh to their sin &
consume their flame,
    bright & swift as a shooting star—
    /it feels good, then hollow
      on the 400th day

    .

if only i could keep it inside
and leave it to die
   /no need to feel fear that way (it's not cheating, *per se*)

     — tell me who am i kidding, again?

    .

(the pills start
   on the 421st day)

    .

what will ever become of you,
     starchild?
   /i still wonder, sometimes
he defines (it
   in) every possibilities— i checked
      on the 434th day

    .

he ate his feelings for breakfast, methinks—
electromagnetic storm preventing from further
robbed observations
    /fuckin' artificial time,
    against me (again, for a change)

.

& i feel quite lethargic on the 518th day, maybe
                  holding back the future sound
        of me giving in— it belongs to the black vastness, now

.

                    (new pills, on the 607th day)

.

i fell asleep to the starship's whispers /
              she was gently humming
              metallic tunes &
                  i had to let it go
        /to the surface, supernova exploding
& debris catching in my eyes—
              the throat again,
outerspace-tetanised

.

                  /& sometimes, pulsar-spasming
thinking of eyes again
              human, so human—
              my biggest misfortune
        /i understood that on the 682nd day

.

703rd day in and it felt like
        the artificial gravity systems were failing
        /tripping on my own mind when
        i sensed him there,
                            waiting

.

t'was only a matter of time before i caved in /
     high on the warm basalt
     that sings through his veins, when only
               stardust-ashes will remain—
as long as they meld into mine, i can't wait

.

                      (i stand on my own
                      on the 720th day)

.

/721st day in & this time, it's frozen warp particles that i cry
     almost as blue as my eyes, he said
          — *a bit more salty, perhaps*

.

(yes, i replied)

PS: bury our corpses under dark matter,
scatter them amongst the stars—
our resting place the rebirth of the universe
(perpetually drifting, together) at last

ANGEL MOUNTAIN
Katherine Gutierrez

For the longest time, I thought that mountains had white peaks because of angels. My father told me so. He said: 'The angels leave their wings there to dry after it rains in the heavens.'

People said I was stupid. Stupid as my father. Stupid as a man who had left one grey morning for his fishing boat and disappeared.

I stopped going to the village school when I was just a child. From then on it was only my mother and me. We ran the little hot tea and coffee shop to the left of the town square.

One morning I found my mother standing under the skylight, pursing her lips.

'Annabelle.' She knew I was there without looking. 'Come see.'

'What is it, mama?'

'It'll be one of those winters, Annabelle-May.'

'How'd you know, mama?'

'Just look at it.' She jutted her chin. 'You can see the steel in the sky.' My mother talked like an old desert fortune-teller sometimes.

In the mornings I would cut a lemon in half and run the juice on the counters to make them gleam like new. My mother made black coffee for us both. We were the only hot drink café in the village and we did pretty well out of it. The Coffee Bean Man who lived by the Frost River was my god-father and, ever since my father had disappeared, he gave my mother all the coffee beans, tea leaves, malt and chocolate she wanted. He always gave me a gift when we visited.

Last time it had been a chocolate goldfish wrapped in dark gold foil. I knew it was chocolate, but it was so pretty I couldn't bear to eat it, so I keep it sewn into the pocket of my apron instead. My mother rolled her eyes when I told her I couldn't eat it, but sometimes I could feel its sly little shape bouncing softly against my leg and it made me feel better somehow.

My mother baked cinnamon cakes. When she brought the morning batch to the table, I turned our sign to OPEN. I didn't even have time to pick up my sponge before the Fur Lady came striding in. Truth be told, I hadn't even seen her approach and our doors are glass and we can see the whole square. But then, everyone did call her a witch.

The Fur Lady was rich and lived in a big peach and red house on the outskirts of town. We all called her the Fur Lady because she was never seen anywhere without her huge black fur hat, black fur stole and her black fur gloves like the paws of a great bear. The first thing the Fur Lady did was to stare at my face. She was taller than any man I'd ever seen.

'Good morning,' she said, and her voice reminded me of my mother's when a customer offended her. All ice.

'Good morning,' I said, clasping my hands and wondering if I should add anything. Usually customers went straight to my mother to do their ordering, and I wasn't sure what the Fur Lady wanted.

My mother came into the dining area at that moment. Her eyes widened at the sight of the Fur Lady, but she nodded politely. 'Well, good morning,' she said. 'What can we get you?'

'A table, first of all. That would be pleasant.' The Fur Lady looked at me reproachfully.

'Which one?' I asked. My mother rolled her eyes high.

'Any one will do,' The Fur Lady said. 'As long as I do, in fact, have one.'

'Don't mind the child,' my mother said. 'She's a little slow.'

I showed the Fur Lady to a table near the window.

'What can I get you?'

'Your finest drinking chocolate,' The Fur Lady said. 'And one of your mother's cinnamon cakes. You can do that, can't you?'

'Drinking chocolate and a cake, is it? Very good, ma'am.'

I retreated into the little back kitchen and gave my mother her order.

'The Fur Lady...' My mother poured hot milk into a jug. 'Why would she be here?' She looked at me as if for answers.

I didn't reply. I fiddled with the lid of the sugar tub.

'Go back and clean the tables if you're going to fidget.'

I went back to my tables. I kept looking at the people wandering past the café door and hoped one of them would enter and then I wouldn't have to make conversation with the Fur Lady. Fortunately, she now seemed uninterested in me, just staring in front of her, eyes narrowed. I thought it was a very strange and rather unsettling way to wait – glaring ahead like that.

My mother came out from the kitchen, her lips pursed. 'We're out of drinking chocolate.' She kept her voice low.

'What was that?' The Fur Lady appeared to have incredible hearing.

My mother almost curtsied. 'We're out of drinking chocolate, ma'am.'

'Well.' The Fur Lady pursed her own lips together. She had a thunderous expression that would rival my mother's. 'That does appear to be a problem.'

'We have cinnamon tea, ma'am. That will go nicely with a cinnamon cake – '

'No, no.' The Fur Lady heaved herself to her feet. 'If there is no drinking chocolate to be found, then it is all for nothing.'

I thought she was being very dramatic and spoilt about a cup of silly old drinking chocolate. We sold coffee first and foremost and she should really do the decent thing and have some of that, instead. My mother looked upset to be losing a rich customer, but there was nothing to be done; we were not due to visit the Coffee Bean Man to replenish our stock for two days.

The Fur Lady wafted toward the door and I was quite glad to see her go.

'Wait,' my mother said. 'Annabelle,' She looked at me with sudden inspiration. 'You still have that chocolate fish your godfather gave you, don't you?'

I twisted the sponge in my hands.

'We could melt that down,' my mother continued.

'Well, that would be most acceptable.' The Fur Lady smiled from behind her stole and made her way back to the table.

'I...I don't have it.' I said. I couldn't remember the last time I'd lied to my mother or a customer. I didn't have much practice at it. The lie came out high-pitched and obvious and my mother's pinched features grew even more drawn.

'Annabelle-May,' she said. 'You will fetch me that chocolate fish now. At once.'

I glanced at the Fur Lady, wondering if this new unpleasantness would convince her to order something else. But she was looking elsewhere, with the polite preoccupation of someone staying out of other people's business.

'I don't have it, mama,' I said. 'The lady will have to order something else.'

My mother's hand shot forward and her little nails dug into my shoulder. 'That's enough,' she hissed. 'Where is that fish?'

'I don't have it anymore, mama. I ate it.'

'I know for a fact you kept it.'

'I ate it, mama.'

My mother regarded me with a chilled look for a few more seconds then whisked away and tramped upstairs. I knew she was rummaging through my room. My fingers touched the chocolate fish concealed in my apron. I glanced at the Fur Lady, to see if she suspected something. She was removing her bear-black gloves, finger by finger.

'I'm afraid ma'am will have to order something else,' I said cheerfully. 'We have a wonderful herb tea. And coconut infused coffee, straight from the silk traders that live by Frost River. I'm sure ma'am will not be disappointed.'

The Fur Lady turned to me with a curving, indulgent smile. She obviously expected my mother to return with my chocolate in hand.

My mother came down the stairs slowly. She narrowed her eyes at me. 'Where did you put it?' she asked, frustrated.

'I ate it, mama.'

She opened her mouth then shut it. She examined me for so long I was half-sure she could see the chocolate fish though my apron. Finally, she crossed her arms. 'You go down to Frost River right now and get some chocolate from the Coffee Bean Man.'

She wanted me to argue, wanted me to be upset because of the distance, wanted to get back at me for being right.

'Of course, mama. I'll just run down and get some.'

She twitched, unhappy with my response. 'I want you back in an hour.'

Seeing as it took an hour to get there, half an hour for the Coffee Bean Man to rifle through his stock and an hour to get back – in good weather – her demand was ludicrous and she knew it. She wanted me to argue and to reveal the chocolate. But I was in no mood to capitulate.

'Of course, mama,' I strolled over to my coat and pulled it around my shoulders. 'I'll be back soon.'

I took one last look at the Fur Lady as I left the café. I'll never forget that face – the smile all melted away and her stony mouth pinched so tightly the lips were white. I could see that she would rather me slip on the ice and break my neck on the way, than have all the drinking chocolate in the world.

I ran out of the café and along the edge of the square, to-ward Frost River. The Angel Mountains were blue and lilac and made of water in the distance. As I ran, I touched the hard shape of the chocolate fish. When I was out of town and safe, I dug my nails into the pocket seams and ripped them, took the foil off the chocolate fish and ate it as I walked. I smiled as I balled the foil up in my hands, feeling clever. I pressed the gold ball into the deep groove of a tree and pushed on through the snow, smiling to myself.

Past the forest, you could see the mountains better. Only I called them Angel Mountains. Just because of what my father told me. I didn't know if they had a real name.

The river pooled in from the east, cutting through a canyon that fell away from the forest to create a great salmon lake, deep within the fir trees. Then it thinned itself and became a river once again, heading straight for the west. Behind the river, was the Coffee Bean Man. He sat in his gold and red caravan, hiding from the cold under piles of silk.

His dog Cero barked at me as I knocked on the caravan door.

'Come, Ann-Belle!' That's what he called me.

When I opened the caravan door the warmth stung my cheeks. The scent of jasmine was strong.

'Just little Ann-Belle today, is it?' The Coffee Bean Man stuck his head out of the silks. He had a wide, white smile and long, dark eyelashes, like a woman's.

'Yes,' I tucked my legs under me and clasped my hands on my lap. The Fur Lady would be waiting, and sharpening herself. 'Mama sent me for some more chocolate.'

'Chocolate?' The Coffee Bean Man twisted onto his back, the silks tangled around his legs.

'She needs more drinking chocolate.'

'Why does she not wait for the usual time?' He kicked his legs to free himself from the silk but the material only clung tighter.

'We have a customer that wants it.'

'Ah.' His dark brows creased. 'I'm afraid I only have your mother's drinking chocolate at the normal time. She must come in two days.'

'I see.' I thought of my mother's fury if I returned without the chocolate and couldn't help wondering if eating the fish had been the best idea.

The Coffee Bean Man noticed my distress. 'Or, perhaps your trip was not wasted!'

I waited.

'You see, Ann-Belle, you could go further.'

'Further?'

'Up the mountain.'

I leaned forward. Nobody ever went near the mountain. That was bad. Especially for girls that were stupid.

'On the peak you will find the people who will give you what you need.' The Coffee Bean Man sat up and crossed his legs. He was wearing yellow clogs with curled toes.

'Who are they?'

'Wanderers. I trade with them. Ink and cloth for their herbs and chocolate.'

'Are they...' I murmured, '...kind people?'

The Coffee Bean Man shrugged. 'There are always ones that are kind and ones that are unkind. Let's hope you meet a kind one.'

So I climbed Angel Mountain.

I kept to a path of black ivy, my feet sinking so deeply into the snow that I did not fear falling. I did not think for one moment of turning back.

I thought of the angels. Angels that dried their wings on mountain ranges.

I could see the path up into the mountains before me, but I could not see myself returning with drinking chocolate for my mother and the Fur Lady. Mama and the Fur Lady seemed very far away, hanging by thin strings on the outskirts of my memory. They seemed to be melting.

My first sight of the angels was not as strange as I thought it would be.

I must have walked for hours because the path at my

back was long and steep and the far tracks already snowed over. I slowed my pace when I heard music. The high hum of some flute.

They were sitting on snow-covered rock, draped in cloth whiter than ice. I watched them for a while. I breathed and listened. Then I went forward, sat in their circle and pressed my hands into the snow. One girl with golden hair nodded at me, but no one else moved or spoke. The last strains of music ended. It lingered in the air and hummed itself away above us. One by one, we stood and began to walk east, into the grey air.

A few folks round town still talk about me.

Stupid, they say. As stupid as her father. Following the angels and never looking back.

BIRTHDAY

Victoria Simpkins

JANINE, mother of MAUDE and STEVE, late fifties.
STEVE, twin of MAUDE, late twenties.
MAUDE, twin of STEVE, late twenties.

The light fades in. End on stage. The stage is a kitchen.
There are half opened cardboard boxes scattered around the
floor. Janine is sitting alone at a round table, a bunch of un-
opened pink peonies sit in a pint glass in the middle of the
table. She stares at them and finishes an unidentified drink
from a tumbler. There are single chairs to her left and right.
Janine gets up and walks centre right to the counter where
there is a sink. She hovers there for a moment then places
the tumbler on the counter. She breathes deeply, grips the
corners of the sink and lets out a small pained moan. Silence
for fifteen seconds. The doorbell rings and she looks at the
clock above the sink. She walks across the stage and opens
the door. Steve walks in, holding a plastic grocery bag containing a bottle. He kisses his mother roughly on the cheek.

JANINE You're early.

STEVE Got a different train.

Steve sits down on the far right chair, takes out the bottle of
whiskey from the bag and slams it down on the table. Janine
rustles in a cupboard.

STEVE Happy birthday.

JANINE I think I have some ready salted somewhere here, from last week when June popped in, she left them, I'm sure they're here.

STEVE [*picks up the whiskey and studies the label*] Couldn't find Monkey Shoulder, that's the stuff that was always in the house, it's pricey too anyway, but the boy on the counter said it was alright, not that he'd know, he looked about thirteen [*guffaws*].

JANINE I said to June that she should have taken them with her, so maybe she did. [*continues to clatter in the cupboard*] I should have got some in, but I thought I already had those leftovers, they might have been stale by now mind, crisps and biscuits are awful when they're stale.

STEVE [*looks over his shoulder*] Mm.

Janine stops rummaging but her hands are still in the cupboard. Pause. Steve turns back round to the table.

STEVE [*looks back at the whiskey in his hand*] But I'm sure it'll taste fine, maybe not something you'd have over ice, but you could have it with a bit of coke or whatever.

JANINE [*closes the cupboard door and sits down*] Look at these beauties Maude got me. [*nods toward flowers and smiles*]

STEVE Roses?

JANINE Peonies.

Steve places the whiskey back on the table.

JANINE I'm off whiskey, off it all really, not even plonk,

doesn't agree with my stomach. I never was much of a whiskey gal, mind you.

Steve leans back in his chair and stares at Janine in silence.

JANINE She sent a lovely card too, had a picture of some sunflowers, goff something.

STEVE Van Gogh.

JANINE Hm, maybe. [*Pause*] I don't think so. I'll ask her later, she's such a clever one, always had an eye for the arts.

Steve scratches his chin with his thumb.

JANINE How's that girl of yours? Joyce?

STEVE Joy.

JANINE Joy?

STEVE Well, I did tell you, we broke up, Joy didn't...

JANINE Joy's a funny name to give a child, isn't it? Wouldn't call your child happy, or sad, would you? No, why not some-thing like Jane? Plain Jane. Why mess around with names, eh? Or, I've always liked Marcia, knew a Marcia once, lovely girl.

STEVE Right.

JANINE Got to use the toilet, love.

Janine gets up and moves upstage right and exits through the door next to the sink. Steve leans forward and rests his elbows on the table. His left knee bobs up and down.

STEVE [*mutters*] Fucking peonies.

The doorbell rings. Steve gets up and opens the same door he arrived through. Maude walks in, carrying a cake in its container. A handbag dangles from her inner elbow. Her hair is a brassy blonde.

MAUDE Oh, you're early? [*Sets cake on counter next to sink*]

Steve sits back down in the chair on the right.

STEVE Different train.

MAUDE Where's Mum?

STEVE Toilet.

MAUDE Did you see Dad last month?

STEVE Yeah, got him some whiskey.

MAUDE He doesn't drink.

STEVE I know that now.

Maude shakes her head.

STEVE What?

Maude picks up the bottle of whiskey.

MAUDE Was this you too?

Janine enters. Maude puts the whiskey bottle back on the table.

MAUDE Mum. [*Hugs Janine. Maude goes to kiss Janine's cheek, Janine holds Maude away by her shoulders*]

JANINE Not too close, got a cold. [*Pause*] Aw, Maudie, you look wonderful. [*Takes a strand of Maude's hair*] Your hair?

MAUDE Mmm, do you like it?

JANINE Oh yes, yes, beautiful dear, makes you glow.

MAUDE Thank you.

STEVE We having cake, or...?

Janine sits down in the middle seat and Maude gets plates out.

MAUDE How was Aunty June's visit, Mum? Did she like the new place?

Maude sits down on the seat to the left.

JANINE Hm? Oh, yes she does, said it was small, but comfortable. She means pokey, but I like it here, it's the right size for one person. Who needs to rattle around that old house anyway, with no one but my magazines to keep me company.

MAUDE I visited you.

JANINE She said she liked the colour in here, called it vanilla. But it's yellow. Don't know what she's on about, this room here is yellow.

Maude cuts the cake into pieces.

STEVE Why are you cutting it all up? We only need three pieces? [*Steve rolls his eyes and gets his phone out from his pocket and plays on it*]

MAUDE Don't you have a proper vase Mum? Instead of that glass?

JANINE No, couldn't find it, must have lost it in the move, bet it was those men, kept eyeing up my stuff, could see them looking at your granddad's silver, bet it's worth a bob or two now. I could see them pricing it.

MAUDE What about the one I bought you last Christmas? From Debenhams?

JANINE Hmm? Oh I don't know, somewhere in the boxes.

Pause as they eat cake in silence.

MAUDE You don't like whiskey, do you Mum?

JANINE What, love? Oh no, love.

MAUDE That's alright, I'll take it for James, you don't mind do you Mum?

STEVE I am here.

Maude stares at Steve.

JANINE Excuse me, just need to nip to the little girls. [*Exit*]

MAUDE Steve.

Pause.

MAUDE [*hisses*] Steve.

Steve looks up from his phone.

MAUDE You could at least pretend.

STEVE What?

Maude sighs.

MAUDE And what's this?

STEVE That is called whiskey, Maude

Silence as they stare at each other.

STEVE Fucking what?

A muffled clunk is heard, then a smash. Maude stands up.

JANINE [*distant*] Whoopsy daisy, don't worry, just a glass!

Maude sits back down, Steve returns to his phone.

MAUDE You're selfish.

STEVE Selfish?

MAUDE I can't believe you've brought whiskey, of all things for her birthday.

STEVE Oh, give it a rest, are we still talking about this?

MAUDE [*shouts*] Yes! [*Pause, lowers voice*] Yes, we are. You seem to be living in a parallel world where it's acceptable [*pause*] to behave like this. Do you really have no empathy? I just don't understand your stupidity.

STEVE What? What are you on about? Empathy for what? For who? Jesus Christ, you're overreacting. She said she doesn't even want it. So take it. Shower it over James, writhe around on the floor together, I don't give a shit. Just stop with this false martyrdom.

Maude stares at Steve.

MAUDE I'm not a martyr, Steve, that doesn't make sense.

STEVE [*groans*] The big man, Mum's saviour, whatever.

MAUDE It's not martyrdom.

STEVE Oh right, I see, yeah, you are the big I am, aren't you? Superior in every way, right Maudie? [*mumble*] Clever little Maudie does it again. Hooray, hoorah you're better than me.

Maude looks away.

STEVE You think because you've been seeing Mum a lot recently you're suddenly her keeper? You didn't care when you fucked off to uni, did you? When they were at each other's throats. Weren't so concerned then, were you?

MAUDE People only swear when they can't articulate themselves properly.

STEVE Fuck off.

They stare at each other without breaking eye contact. Janine enters and stumbles.

MAUDE Mum?

JANINE Hm? Oh sorry, such a clutz. [*Giggles*]

Maude stands up.

MAUDE Mum?

Janine sits down at the table and starts smoking.

MAUDE I thought you'd given up?

JANINE I have. [*Pause*]

JANINE That hair, love. It doesn't [*pause*] it doesn't suit you. Looks cheap. Why don't you go to my old, uhm, my old one? Jerry's girl, the one with the harelip, she does a good job.

MAUDE I thought you liked it?

JANINE No, love, makes you look [*waves hand with cigarette in Maude's direction*] a bit like a crack addict. [*Laughs*]

Steve looks up at Maude. Janine stands up and sways a little, gets three glasses from the cupboard and puts them on the table.

JANINE Let's celebrate! It is my birthday after all.

Maude places her hand on Janine's wrist.

MAUDE Why don't we have some more cake instead?

Janine snatches her hand away, pours herself a large glass of whiskey, downs it and repeats. She puts out the cigarette in one of the empty glasses.

STEVE You're alright, aren't you Mum?

JANINE What? What a stupid thing to say. Of course I'm fine. It's my birthday. Let's have some fun. Where's the music? It's so dead in here, come on, you're both young. You're meant to be out-partying me, you boring old farts. [*Exits*]

Maude sits down and scratches her chin with her thumb.

MAUDE I have to go make sure she's okay.

STEVE She'll be fine, stop patronising her.

MAUDE No, Steve. She won't. Last month before she moved out she got so drunk she fell down the stairs and knocked herself out. Aunt June found her. Crumpled at the bottom of the stairs.

STEVE You're so dramatic.

MAUDE Steve, this is really serious.

STEVE She's just been a bit low since splitting with Dad, it's a blip.

MAUDE A bit low? [*Pause*] A blip?

STEVE I know what I said, anyway it's her birthday.

MAUDE She's been a mess, not that you'd know, when was the last time you called, let alone visited her?

STEVE [*snorts*] That's rich.

MAUDE It isn't really though, is it?

STEVE Really? Oh well, of course you're right, yet again.

MAUDE You'll always be bitter.

STEVE And you'll always be a cold bitch.

Silence. Maude plays with the wedding ring on her finger.

MAUDE I just [*pause*] I needed to get away.

STEVE And I didn't?

MAUDE I was terrified of turning into them.

STEVE And you had to go all the way to Scotland for that?

Janine enters with a radio, visibly drunker. She puts the radio down on the table and it knocks the flowers off. They smash on the floor.

JANINE [*slurring*] Oh. [*Pause*] Who put those there, stupid [*pause*] things.

MAUDE [*holds Janine's arm*] Mum, let's get you to bed?

JANINE Get off me, I'm fine, get off.

STEVE What about the flowers?

MAUDE Come on, why don't we look through those photos you were showing me the other day? Of me and Steve, in Spain? You liked them, didn't you? They're in your room, shall we go in there?

STEVE Stop talking to her like she's five.

MAUDE Shut up.

JANINE Who's five? Oh Stevie, look at you, growing into, growing into a man. You look more and more like your father every time I see you. The bastard. The filthy bastard.

MAUDE Mum, please.

JANINE You know he cheated on me when you were both five, that whore from work, the one with those sapphire earrings dangling all over the place. I took him back [*takes a swig from the whiskey bottle*] I took that bastard back and now I'm alone. I could have started again, could have run away to [*pause*] to Cornwall! Could have had a life, instead of this [*waves the bottle in the audience's direction*] all of this. Now I'm here in this godforsaken room, this vanilla room. Vanilla. [*Scoffs*]

STEVE My train is soon, I've got to head off. [*Gets up*]

JANINE Oh Stevie, such a short visit, come next week, why don't you? Come next week?

STEVE Uh, well...

JANINE I need a nap now, take me to my room, Stevie, I'll show you a picture I found the other day of you, you're so sweet, let me show you.

Steve looks at Maude, then at Janine. Scratches his chin with his thumb and nods.

JANINE [*hugs Maude*] Good night, you're a good girl Maudie, say hi to James, won't you. [*Kisses Maude on the forehead*]

Steve and Janine exit.

Maude begins to play with her wedding ring.

Fade out.

Fade in

A door is centre stage, it is spot-lit. Maude and Steve sit on the floor, their backs against the door, not looking at each other.

STEVE Will she be okay in there?

MAUDE Yeah, she'll probably sleep till the morning now.

[*Pause*]

STEVE How long has it been like this?

MAUDE About a year.

STEVE Is it [*pause*] often?

MAUDE I'm helping her.

Steve nods. Pause.

MAUDE James and I are getting a divorce.

STEVE What?

MAUDE I don't think we love each other anymore.

STEVE I'm sorry.

MAUDE It's okay, it's been a long time coming.

STEVE No, not about that. I mean yeah, I am sorry for that, but, uhm, I'm sorry for today. [*Pause*] The past couple of [*pause*] I'm just sorry.

Maude turns to Steve who carries on looking at the audience.

STEVE I know I'm a shit.

MAUDE Sometimes.

They both smile.

STEVE Joy said she couldn't love someone who didn't love themselves.

MAUDE What a cliché.

Steve laughs. Maude looks back into the audience. Pause.

MAUDE James said we didn't know each other anymore. I guess that's fair, I mean, I'm not sure of myself most of the time, I just really... [*looks at Steve*]

MAUDE I became them, didn't I?

STEVE Mum and Dad?

MAUDE Mhm.

STEVE No, you didn't.

Pause.

STEVE Are you going home?

MAUDE No, I want to make sure she's okay. I don't want her to wake up alone in the morning.

STEVE Okay. [*Pause*] I'll stay, too.

Maude takes Steve's hand in hers.

MAUDE Thanks.

Fade out.

THIS POEM WANTS TO BE A LESBIAN COUNTRY SONG SO BAD

[AFTER KIM ADDONIZIO]

Erica Gillingham

This poem wants to croon
from the tape deck in your pick-up truck
down that red dirt road
as you make your way to the honky-tonk
on a Saturday night,
your girl straddling the stick-shift.

It wants to be kicked and stomped
into the hardwood floor of the bar
drip with your sweat, your tequila, your beer,
and find you in the bathroom stall:
hands against the wall,
belt-buckle clanging against concrete,
your girl do-se-do-ing you between rounds
cause you're here for the party.

This poem wants to sneak
onto the juke-box like the river run dry
as you slip out the back door,
drive up to the mountain clearing,
and play loud and long
while you make love
under the stripes of the white moonlight
and the blanket made of stars.

FIRE

Fionnuala Bland

The world growled. Bethia shuddered and dropped her needle and thread. She glanced at the pair of worn shoes hanging from a nail in a corner of the small sitting room. They would protect her, she thought. Help keep the bad spirits away.

She gathered her sewing from the wooden floorboards and began again, jabbing the brown thread into the needle's eye, thrusting the needle into the quilt. Her brother Alexander was upstairs, asleep under thin blankets. The room where their parents had slept last spring was the warmest in the house.

Ever since her mother died, Bethia had been thinking about fire. Fire to warm Alexander. Fire to warm herself. Fire had always fascinated her: the way it fidgeted, as if agitated. *Nowhere near it*, Mother had said. *Do you hear me, Bethia?* She'd tried to light a candle when she was nine, Lord, six year ago that was now! Her mother's face had turned as bright as the blaze. *You could have set the whole of Anstruther alight!*

Matters were different now, surely?

The Lord will provide. She could still hear Mother's voice in the cold house. Mary Brower had been a good Christian woman, and undeserving of her death, but women were not supposed to show intelligence, tell magic tales, or give remedies to the sick.

A week of torture for witchcraft and a slow execution at the stake. She had not seen her mother's final moments, had lain with Alexander instead, in their parents' bed, holding him tight. He was only five. Their father died soon after. Blair said it was the influenza, coughing up his guts. But

Bethia thought it was the smell of her mother's body that killed him, lingering over their small village for days.

Rain crashed into the slate roof, the stone walls, the shuddering windows. Bethia chanted the Lord's Prayer until all she could hear was her own voice. Only a banging at the door pulled her from her reverie.

Her best friend and neighbour, Eirica Reid, was standing on the porch, clutching a covered bucket. Her hood veiled her tiny face in shadow.

'Good evening, Bethia.' The storm muffled her voice.

'Get you in,' gasped Bethia. She let Eirica slip past and forced the door shut behind her. What was she doing out so late, and the storm so wild?

'Father sent me to give you this.' Eirica hesitated, and then placed her bucket in the open fireplace. 'I know your mother never liked fire but she is not here and it is too cold tonight. You will surely freeze without one.' She let down her hood, revealing a mop of fair hair tied into a bun.

Bethia eyed the bucket, where the embers dwindled and gasped for wood. It was cold. And Mother was with God. What good had her wisdom brought her?

'Try,' said Eirica. Her face was wet.

Bethia clutched her dirty cotton skirts and crept toward the embers. The flames gushed hot air into her face and she leapt back. The fire shrank, still flickering with orange life. Bethia forgot the storm, forgot her caution, forgot Eirica gaping at her. She advanced again, drinking in the warmth. The glow stretched toward her, dancing an inch from her face. Bethia relaxed, letting her pale shoulders slacken and her grey eyes soften. She had done this before, playing with fire, fire playing with her. With that candle. At strangers' hearths when Mother wasn't looking. Who knew how to control a child who felt fire in her very skin?

She sat cross-legged in front of the small conflagration. The embers fell back. Bethia cocked her head. The flames tilted the same way. She grinned, twirling her finger. The flickers pirouetted. She had never been able to do this so openly, not even with her closest friend. But this house was hers, now.

Eirica gasped. 'God have mercy. How do you do that?'

Bethia shrugged. She stood up, lightheaded with warmth and power. The flames stretched to match her height.

Eirica's grin wavered. 'Know you what will happen if word spreads of this?'

'*I am not a witch!*'

Bethia turned away from the fire and fought welling tears. She could not sit here playing. She had a younger brother to look after and a quilt to sew. 'You must leave. Your family will be wondering what has kept you.' She followed Eirica to the door, helping her with her hood. Her friend grasped her arm.

'Blair is to be burned tomorrow. I know this hurts you. Keep back from the fire, Bethia. I did not know you had this...*way*.'

'I will stand at the back.'

'I would that I could,' Eirica sighed. 'Father pulls us forward.' Her sallow cheeks grew even paler and for a moment, Bethia thought she was going to vomit or cry. Eirica forced a smile and pulled her cloak tighter around her chest. 'Good evening, Bethia.'

They wrenched the door open together. Behind them, the fire sputtered and sighed under the sound of the dying storm.

Blair had been a good neighbour, and a friend. She had knitted dolls for her when she was seven; given her potatoes and grain after Mother was killed. She had concocted remedies for sicknesses and tended to influenza victims everyone else avoided, for fear of infection. She had tried to rescue Father with her herbal medicine. It had not worked. He died choking on his bloody vomit.

She was sickened she had to go, but it was not safe to stay away. The village had not forced her to watch her own mother die, but they would expect all good Christian souls tomorrow. They were the progeny of a proven witch and people would gossip at their absence. *She has something to hide. She takes after her mother.* She would hang back, and block Alexander's ears. The sound of them cheering her mother's death had left her shaking and sleepless ever since.

The storm scared away the morning sun. Clouds drizzled over the seaside town. Mother used to say raindrops were God's tears. No wonder why He was crying today.

Bethia pulled on her cloak. 'Alexander! It is time to go!'

Her brother's head appeared at the top of the stairs. His chestnut hair stood in tufts, scruffy and unwashed. Tears, hunger and nightmares had drawn the blood from his face, leaving it ashen, except for his red-rimmed eyes.

'I would not go.'

'I would not, either. But we must.' Alexander sloped down the stairs, his skinny body drooping. She wished she could wilt, but she had to act strong for the both of them. She took a breath and let it out slowly. As long as she remained calm, so would he. She wrapped him in his cloak and kissed his head. 'Good boy.'

It was as if Pittenweem, the neighbouring fishing village, already reeked of singeing hair and skin. They reached the mismatched stones of the priory's wall, a hundred shades of brown and grey. Bethia spotted the Reids a few paces ahead. Eirica saw her and smiled sadly. Bethia grimaced. She could hear the murmur of the crowd behind the wall. She moved Alexander closer to her, but the boy wriggled, his eyes wide. She took his hand, and he let her hold it. They cut through an iron gate marking the east entrance, nearly colliding with the hooded throng.

Bethia clutched Alexander's hand, moving them to the edge of the crowd. 'Stay you with me,' she said. 'I would not lose you here.' Alexander sniffed. She recognised Eirica's fisherman father, Peter, standing in front of them. He was six foot four and cushioned with muscle. He turned and saw them.

'Can you see, child? Get you to the front.'

She stared into his kind eyes, wanting to strike him. She could not stay at the back now he had invited her forward. A kindness, some would say. She smiled through gritted teeth and edged in front of him, pulling Alexander with her. They now stood in the heart of the throng, four rows from the front. Still safe from the fire but too close to avoid seeing the stake.

Through the gaps in the mob she could see Father Phillip. He was standing at the pit, a grassless dip blackened from previous burnings. He was not alone; he was dragging a woman. Emaciated, ragged. She saw that it was Blair.

Around Bethia, the mob hissed and jeered. Some spat at the thin woman, a tangle of bones and bruises slumped in the dirt. Bethia wanted to vomit. She could barely recognise the good woman who had taken care of her. Beside her, Alexander rocked and swayed with the noisy crowd.

'I would not see this, Bethia,' the boy whispered. She saw a pain in his eyes as he looked between her and the fire.

She knew he was remembering their mother's words. *Do not you fear, my children. I love you.* But how could they not fear when even their protector was taken? How could they stand amongst old friends that had cheered her murder?

She was learning not to cry in front of her brother. It would only make him more frightened. She gave his hand a squeeze and stepped to the right, pulling him with her, so that the family in front obstructed his view.

But she could see everything.

A hooded man strode into view. The judge. He towered over Blair, his face chubby and solemn.

'Blair Ross, you are convicted of witchcraft and consorting with the Devil.'

Bethia could see the smirk on his lips. He was relishing the power. She clenched her teeth, restraining herself from shouting out and damning them all.

Two men, one carrying a length of rope, closed in on

the old woman. They took one arm each, hauled her to her feet and bound her to the stake. She moaned.

'Say you the Lord's Prayer without fault and you are free to go,' the judge said. Blair opened her mouth, but could only choke. Bethia wanted to cry. Why were they not letting her reply? She needed time. Had they beaten her?

The judge nodded to the waiting men. They snaked the rope around her neck and tied it to the wood. Blair gasped, half-strangled.

The men began to scrape flints together, creating a frantic rhythm. The old woman was like a child next to the judge: tiny, whimpering. Bethia dropped Alexander's hand and clenched her fists. She could not stay silent.

'You cannot do this! Blair has saved lives, not taken them!'

The mob pivoted. Bethia glimpsed Eirica's frightened face. She felt the shove of strangers as she pushed through the crowd. Hands tried to grasp her but she pushed them away. 'She is innocent!'

The judge snatched her arm as she approached the stake. 'Child, what are you doing? What is your proof?'

'What is *yours*?' She pulled herself from his grip. She did not even know if Blair could hear or see her. Her head lolled, dark hair covering her face.

One of the waiting men seized Bethia. Before she could steady herself or fight back, he threw her to the ground. The flint sparks ignited. Her attacker stumbled backwards. Flames bit into his legs, pushing him toward the crowd. The glow rose inside Bethia. She clambered to her feet, moving closer to Blair. The woman raised her head, seemed to recognise her. The flames grew with Bethia, a blazing wall, towering over the now running crowd. She pulled at Blair's ropes desperately, fingers aching. Blair groaned, trying to help her. The ropes, old and stiff, seemed to crumble under the bright flames. Fell away.

Fast feet on ground. Her fury dissolved into fear. Fear of

them catching her. Fear for Alexander: what would they do to him? Rain saturated her skirts, forcing her to run with them bunched in her hand. The wind whipped her hood back, rain soaking her face and hair. She prayed the weather would not kill the fire she had set behind her. She needed as much time as it could give her.

She ran until her breath drowned inside the wind and her clothes were heavy with water. Her shoulders sagged, her head thumped and feet stumbled. Odd shapes came into vision. Caves, defying the wind and rain. She clambered to-ward them, a few yards uphill from the path, and slipped into one of the coves.

The quiet gloom comforted her, blocking the world. She lay down at the back of the cave, the damp from her clothes seeping into her skin. She wished her mother was here with her now, to comfort her, to tell her what to do. She could al-most feel the warmth of her arms around her as she closed her eyes, could almost hear the whispered assurances that she was safe here, that no one would find her in the dark.

She woke to the sound of prayer. A monotonous chant, grow-ing louder. It matched the rhythm of footsteps on gravel. Bethia clamped her mouth shut. She shuffled to the cave's darkest corner, hugging her knees to her chest.

'Our Father, who art in Heaven.'

How many were there? Were her friends chanting amongst them? People changed with one smell of witchcraft. Brothers against sisters, husbands against wives, neighbours against allies. She wondered where Alexander was; had someone taken him to safety?

Cold crawled around her limbs, clinging to her skin.

Please, God, don't let them find me.

She could hear footsteps nearer, echoing through the cave. *Please, God.*

Father Phillip appeared. He was carrying a large crucifix that glinted in the dimness. He shoved it forward as he saw her. 'Satan, get thee hence!'

Bethia glared at him. 'I am not of Satan!'

'You controlled Hell's fire, released a witch before us, yet deny consorting with the Devil?'

'I am a good Christian, Father. You know this.' She wanted to scream. He had christened her, blessed her, witnessed her seated in Church, week after week. Even after he had murdered her mother.

'Then why do you hide?' he said.

Her temper snapped. 'Because you would not believe me, either way. Once you suspect someone, you deem their every action a crime against God.'

The priest gasped, stepped backwards as if she had cursed him.

'Dare you insult the teachings of the Bible, Miss Clark?'

His shout summoned the others. People swarmed the cave, yelling when they saw her. Peter Reid was with them; he yanked her from the ground. Bethia cried out; it felt as if her bones would crack in his grip.

'Brother Reid,' she said. 'Please! You are my neighbour, my father's kinsman—'

His face was shut and hard.

After a while, Bethia forgot she was screaming. Her cries had become her breath, a normal thing, mixed with the wind.

Peter could have carried her in one arm. Instead, he dragged her. Her knees scraped the gravel, her skirt soaked with rain and blood. The mob marched with them, pelting her with stones and spit. They kicked and trampled her, hissing and praying until they reached Anstruther harbour.

She retched blood. She wanted to cry but crying hurt her ribs. She wanted to run but her legs could not move. She closed her eyes against their maddened faces. Rough hands tied rope around her waist, making her a human puppet. She opened her eyes. Peter was standing in a wooden boat, untying it from the jetty. Dread soaked her. They had tethered her to the back of the boat.

Water. Waves like teeth, ready to devour her. She scrabbled with the rope ineffectually, trembling, unsure whether with cold, pain or terror.

A scream cut the air. '*Fire!*'

Bethia pivoted. Her tormentors stared back toward the town. It was the Reids' house, glowing with flames. Smoke blackened the clouds. Fire snared the neighbouring houses as screams moved through the mob. Peter leaped from the boat and sprinted to the harbour, shouting for buckets and help.

Bethia attacked her rope again, desperate to escape while the fire distracted them. The crowd dispersed, a few people scrambling to the nearest buildings for fire hooks to tear down the inflamed roofs before the blaze could spread. Bethia's rope loosened. She tugged it over her head and looked back toward the fire. The smoke, the promised warmth, enticed her, strengthened her, igniting that familiar glow. She stumbled to her feet.

'It is her!' A woman pointed at Bethia. 'She is bewitching the fire!'

Perhaps she was.

Every step she winced, every step she glowed. She stumbled past villagers, handing along brimming buckets in a human chain from the harbour to the fire. Bethia moved faster. She could run away and save herself. But she did not know where Eirica and Alexander were. Blair. She could not leave them to burn, and the flames might yet listen to her.

The inferno drew her in.

Smoke snaked into her nostrils, into her eyes, into her mouth. She choked, spluttering more blood. She reached the Reids'. More a furnace than a house.

Beside it, the charred remains of her own family home. Horror suffocated her. Alexander. She hurried around the blaze, searching. The flames moved with her, growing, shrinking, dancing like acrobats.

'Bethia!' She turned. Eirica stood metres away, her arm

around Alexander. The flames sparked as Bethia laughed with relief. She embraced her friend, fighting tears and hoping her swollen face would not scare her brother.

'Heavens! Your face, Bethia! Are you alright?' Eirica reached a tentative hand to her cheek.

She disguised the pain with a smile. 'Do not you worry about me. I was afraid you had been burned alive!'

Alexander smiled shakily as he looked up at her, his bony arms clinging to her waist. 'Eirica did it.'

Bethia frowned. 'Did what?'

'I set the fire,' Eirica said, her voice low. 'I was frightened for you and I knew I had to do something to distract them. I am glad I did now.' Her eyes lingered on Bethia's face.

For a moment, Bethia could not speak. 'You set your own house on fire?'

'It is not my house. It is my father's. And he does not deserve a home anymore.' Her eyes saddened. 'He is not the father I knew.'

They watched the hoard of men attacking the furnace with water. Others tore at the fabric of their houses to stop the fire from spreading. Their buckets were too small. Half the town was flaming. They had to flee, before the fire died and the search started. They would stone her, torture her, drown her, all of them. She would escape with Eirica and Alexander and forget the village.

She turned back to Eirica. 'What of Blair?'

Her friend shook her head, eyes searching her own. 'We must leave, Bethia. Now.'

Still, she could not move. She watched her neighbours, stumbling through the smoke. A boy even younger than Alexander stood amongst the rushing crowd, crying. No one was paying him any heed. Where was his mother?

'Come, Bethia! Before they catch us!'

She knew what she should do, but she found herself walking back toward the furnace. The blaze bowed before her. A thrill coursed through her. She could make it do anything. If only she could find Father Phillip, Peter Reid. The judge. How she would laugh to watch them smoulder. It would not surprise her if they were hiding away, cowering in their boat, watching the faithful burn.

Eirica shook her shoulder. *'Bethia!'*

Bethia glanced toward Alexander, standing amongst the smoke, shaking with tears. She took a choking breath. Alexander must live; so must all innocents. She would not have the place they had loved lost to the belly of the flame. She was his sister. Not a killer.

She turned away from them and ran back through the crowd.

Bethia perched at the harbour's edge. The grey waves chewed the stone. Seagulls screeched in the wind. Orange flames licked her skirts. It had followed her; like a sweetheart. She was surprised to find there was no pain. She glanced at the smoky sky, praying her plan would work.

And jumped.

MOVEMENT

Karoline Vembre

Waiting

It is whisky and the nature of the wild. And the wind that carries the daisy petals. And the wind in the waiting room slightly sober slightly somebody.

It is standing by walls waiting. Standing with relentless anonymity, watching rain and paint peeling. Pain prickling pebble stones and disappointment.

Whisky eyes expiring. Veiled and or washed.

Waiting and a little white.

Walking in

Where, here. Hear the breaking low base laughter and the morning after. Hear wet ground through the hometown. Hear, where the streetlights went out for a glass of wine and a siren silenced the drunken feet.

Tunnel lights circle thunder in blackbird eyes. Off smells and stains and orchids there are illumination. Like smokes and trains.

Seeing

Ash falls and eyes cut in burn.

Ash comes as it likes comes as it likes. What met her pierced white spots and dried eye. Ash falls into sandpaper grain.

Errors arise arouse a rise toward. What met her sees her see. See her see what she saw and sink.

Eyes see shut. Shut between legs. As a matter of falls facts fake. Fingers between legs. Shut more, no wait. White fingers between legs. Eyes see eyes see. Between ash and white and ash and white and eyes. She see, it burns.

Deciding

Wait for me. Unshiver your voice with shallow thought. Mind up maker meet me drunk and deluded, discussing. Tell me tell me over talk me over talking me sober. Not now not right now not now now right now now.

Love him if he close the door and close the other. If he close it. If he close it if did he if he did if he close it. Cough it. Coughing it up. Coughing him up I will put a sigh in all of them, any so. Button is nearly there. But he is nearly there. Nearly button him there. Opening him to say, to say oh no to say my sister. Say I choke. Say I choke the other all of them, any so.

Walking out

Say it with flower or say it with flowers. Or say it with flowers or with dirt. With winter the waiting bed. The cold cotton quilt. Guilt it spills. It comes and it is as it seems it comes. Regret it is. Reject the postman.

Again again he sends rephrasing refreshing retelling, wrong spelling.

Books are beds and night-time flowers. Swallow the core and the paper. Licks the ink. The erotica. Touch the rain covered lightly. Covered lightly in dirt and touch.

If he comes here, say, If he comes here. Say, I walked. I

walked the opposite. Say If he comes, I say.

Beginning

To be a millimetre. A sigh in a multitude. A brick. A beginning. A break down, my dear.
    The break is the length of the beginning. The beginning
begun. Begun a gun. Sigh and run irretrievably undone oh
run. Flower bud shatter and blood spatter chitter-chatter.
    Holes in wall paper white and spotted. Flowers peeling
off, pluck the brain.
    Its thinking. Its thin, it's the king. Between maybe between
whether or not or not now. Between me and meeting. Its
needless to day. Say we need less to day. Begin with now
with without with within with chaos and then begin. With
now we know nothing with now we can be and begin.

RUNNING AWAY

Elliot Codling

James had run away. Again. It was almost becoming routine. At first, there had been reasons for the running: an argument or a fight. But now it just happened. He went out in the morning and at night he didn't go home. Sometimes it wasn't even a conscious decision. He slept wherever. It wasn't a dangerous neighbourhood. Sometimes he stole things from shops. Never anything big and never anything he really needed. Sometimes he scratched cars down the side with a coin or a key. He didn't know the owners and the cars weren't anything special, he even hated the noise the coin made, as he did it. He never got caught, though he never took any particular precautions. Once, he joined up with a group of other kids and they went to three of the abandoned farm houses that lay just outside of town and threw rocks through the windows. That got boring quickly.

Running away never got boring. Or maybe it did, but he didn't stop doing it. He went somewhere different each time. He told everyone he wouldn't come back. Well, that wasn't strictly true; he didn't speak to anyone about it, but he did tell himself he would never come back. It was always a lie.

This time he left town by the back road, the one used by coal miners thirty years ago, which ran out to a few pathetic villages. He climbed a hill in the setting sun, trying to catch up to his shadow as it lengthened. The tops of the hills around him were surprisingly flat, and he could see for miles. The whole town was laid out for him. He could see people, small as insects, crawling their way home and lights coming on in houses and car headlights roving this way and that, like search lights. He sat on the lip of the hill and watched the quiet stars appear. This was the time he liked best. When everything was quiet. The birds had flown back to their nests, the bugs had settled down to sleep and people were sitting down to dinner. He counted the streets and tried to work out which house was his, but it was too hard to tell. They all looked the same.

It was full dark before James decided he wouldn't be going home that night. He'd thought of running away earlier that day, but you could never be sure until night came. Sometimes he'd wake up and it wouldn't even be midnight yet and he would slink home and no one would realise he'd run away that day. Not this time, though. He'd come too far. In fact, he'd never run this far away before. It would be very hard to climb down in the dark. He could slip and break his leg or his neck. That was his Mum's favourite phrase when he was younger. 'Stop that before you break your neck!' she would shout and rush to drag him away from whatever fun he was trying to have. 'It's not fair,' he'd protest. That was his favourite phrase. 'Nothing's fair,' she'd say.

James heard it so much, he started believing it. He looked around at other kids his age, with the newest toys, Gameboys and Nintendos, and their clothes never seemed too small and their shoes were never falling apart. They had crisps and grapes in their lunch boxes. All James ever had was a beef paste sandwich. He hated beef paste. It tasted like cat sick. Even his sister, Katy, seemed better off. She was two years younger, only eleven, but she got fancy hairbands and nice dresses and if ever there was an apple to spare it was hers.

'It's not fair,' James told her once.

'Nothing's fair,' she replied.

The sun had set completely and it started to get cold. James shivered. He only had his thin jacket. It was spring, but only just. By the light of the stars he found his way to a large tree, buds of leaves showing on the branches. It wasn't the best shelter but it was better than nothing.

The roots made lying down uncomfortable, but after a lot of wriggling, he managed to find a position. He dug around in his pockets for his small tobacco pouch.

Sam had taught him to smoke and given him his first cigarette in the blind spot of the car park at school where they couldn't see you from the staff room. James choked the first time but it got better after that. He didn't really like smoking, but Sam did and he liked Sam. Sam wore a big overcoat with so many pockets sometimes had to search for ten minutes or more to find things. He filled the pockets whenever he went into a store and shared the loot with James. Sam was different to most other kids. When James told him that he'd run away, Sam shrugged. 'So what?' he asked. James had no good answer.

Sam ran away too, but he ran away properly. He went and never came back. At first James was sure he would turn up again. It was hard, running away. You got cold and hungry really fast. But Sam didn't come back. Two weeks after he left, Mum came to see James in his room. She didn't knock. She told him Sam wasn't coming back and he said 'So what?' and she left. That's what Sam would have said, and saying it made it easier not to care. Since Sam left there was no one for James to talk to. The other kids laughed at him. The way he looked. The way he smelled. Just the way he was.

A cool wind came over the hill. Raindrops began pattering off his face and clothes. He cursed. That was something he'd done: taught Sam how to curse properly. Mum was a master at it. He'd overheard a teacher saying Mum could curse for Britain in the Olympics. James wished there was an Olympian cursing event. He pulled his jacket up over his head, but that left his tummy exposed. He shuffled as close to the tree as he could and closed his eyes, determined to sleep. It took a long time.

He awoke as the sky began to lighten. It had stopped raining but the clouds were thick and made the light a dim grey. The world seemed old. James straightened out his body. He had to do it slow because his joints ached so much. He was soaked from head to foot, and colder than he'd ever felt. It had rained a few times when he ran away before but there was always a bus shelter or a doorway to hide in. The tree hadn't helped at all, its bare branches carried on dripping water long after the rain had stopped. James ran his hand down one of the roots, dug at it with his fingers, wondering how deep it went.

Sitting up was an ordeal. His head throbbed and his teeth chattered. He fished out his tobacco and started at the sight of his own hands. They were an awful purple colour with little blotches of orange. He rubbed them together. They reminded him of dead and rotting things. He hoped chunks wouldn't fall off as he warmed up. They didn't, but the purple didn't fade either. He managed to make a roll-up without spilling too much tobacco. He picked some of his favourite curse words to say when the lighter wouldn't work. On the sixth try the flame took and he inhaled deeply, feeling the warmth fill his chest and spread to his fingertips. He could imagine himself filling with smoke, turning into smoke, and floating away over the hills. Maybe not over the hills, they didn't really lead anywhere. Nothing seemed to lead anywhere. Maybe that was why he always went home.

James stood up, joints popping. The rain had stopped but the mist was so thick it was hard to make out the town. People would just be waking up, getting hot showers and sweet cereals. He wasn't sure how he knew this but he knew it. 'It's not fair,' he said, as his stomach rumbled.

In autumn he used to take Katy to raid the hedges for blackberries. There were thousands of them and sometimes Mum would give them a bowl to fill and they would return with their hands and faces covered in sticky, purple juice. It was a long time since he and Katy had done anything together. When Katy got upset she cried and when she cried Mum got angry. It didn't matter if he was right or wrong, it was always his fault. Katy knew it too: she would threaten him or just start bawling for no reason and then giggle when Mum cursed.

That's why he'd run away this time. Katy had gotten some money for her birthday and spent it going to the cinema with her friends. They weren't meant to go, Mum had forbidden it, but she snuck out. The next day Mum asked what she'd spent her money on. Katy stuck out her lip and pointed right at James.

'*He* took it off me!' she screeched, her face already red and big tears streaming down her cheeks.

'Did *not!*' He was appalled.

'Did too!'

'*Did not!*'

Mum demanded James give her the money back. James refused. Mum tweaked his ear until he went to his room and got the box out from under his bed where he kept the scraps of money he managed to save and counted out fifteen pounds. As soon as they left him alone he'd scooped the rest into an old sock, put it in his pocket and run away.

James finished his cigarette and made himself another. He was almost out of tobacco, he would have to get some more. He wondered where Sam had gone and if things were any different for him. Maybe he had enough money for tobacco and something better than toast for breakfast. The lighter sparked on the second try this time. Birds trilled and in the distance James could hear cars starting up. The second cigarette didn't taste as good. The magic feeling of turning to smoke and escaping was all gone. He stubbed out the cigarette and began to carefully make his way down the hill.

WE STILL SOMETIMES HEAR THEM

Sean Wai Keung

Nothing was pretty
about that life.

We would wake up to sounds
of live pigs hanging
with holes in necks.

We watched the neighbour
collect their warm blood
in pans.
Nothing would be wasted

not even words
all talking superfluous
under that fountain of squeals.

There was nothing we could do.
So we returned to bed
without looking at each other

& imagined where we would be
in fifteen years' time.

UGLY
Haley Jenkins

Eliza didn't enjoy the Internet. She knew how to use it, but after all the hacking scandals, Facebook arrests and virus disasters covered in *The Independent*, she preferred to spend her time in the garden.

Still, she had to use the humming thing to figure out what kind of robot had started living in her shed.

'Cyborg' seemed to suit it best, according to nameyourmonsters.co.uk. Half human, half machine. Eliza leaned back in her mahogany chair, glancing out of the patio door windows. The blue shed sat on the left side of her garden, astride her greenhouse and in front of her potato plot. She couldn't see any movement.

She'd found the cyborg at 7.30 that morning, during the cool and quiet hours. She'd gone out to fetch her tool basket from the shed and almost missed it, huddled under some loose tarpaulin in the right hand corner. It was only when Eliza knocked over a ball of garden string that the poor thing flinched. Thousands of little LED lights flickered on, glittering across the cyborg's skin, like sugar. Eliza felt more fascinated than frightened. She remembered how the faerie lights had twinkled in the trees at her retirement party.

The university's art department had saved up and booked a fancy venue, with a lovely outdoor banquet table. They did it up like the Mad Hatter's tea party in *Alice in Wonderland*. Someone even let a few mice loose on the table after dinner.

Eliza sighed and paced about the room. She had loved her job, an art professor teaching eager, malleable minds.

She still had her clays, her watercolours, oils, acrylics, and bits and bobs to create her art. Half the day in the garden, half the day in her studio. But the cyborg had more art about it than anything she had ever seen. Her whole collection, the paintings, the sculptures, all of it dulled compared to that silvery thing in her shed.

It must have come late in the night, yes that had to be it. She'd been gardening until 8pm and she hadn't seen it when she put her tools away.

'But what do I do with you now?' Eliza spoke aloud. 'Someone must be looking for you, there is always someone.'

She had locked the shed door after seeing it, and waited for splintering wood and thumping feet. But that was three hours ago and the shed remained intact. Not a peep. Perhaps it wanted to stay hidden. Maybe fear kept it inside? In the movies things that looked like that always ran. Or attacked you.

Eliza went up to her bedroom and dug out an old, green hooded jumper and saggy trousers. She stuffed them into a backpack and went back down into the kitchen. Did cyborgs eat? She supposed it could, if it still had a human digestive system. But why would anyone want to keep *that* of all things? If she'd been able to get rid of her seventy-one year old bladder she would have, then burned it and used the ash in the garden.

She packaged a chicken panini, just in case the cyborg was a bit thick and had kept its belly.

Eliza walked past the strawberry, carrot and the potato beds, up to the shed door and pressed her right ear against it, her silver stud scraping against the wood. No sound. She took the key out of her pocket, fitted it into the lock and opened the door.

The cyborg had moved. It was sitting on her wicker chair, turning a sparkly pink photo frame over in its hands. And what hands! They looked just like a human skeleton, but twice the size. Poetry had been tattooed into the bone, all the way to the mid-wrist. The letters were curving, delicate and old-fashioned, curling around the fingers like corn snakes.

Its face looked quite human, except for the eyes, which were empty skull-sockets. Most of the lights had been wired into its silvery head. The face seemed to be a young girl's, about twelve years old.

The cyborg had to be six foot six or seven: even sitting it had to bend its head to its chest. The little lights formed patterns all over it, reminding her of simple Indian mendhi. Most of it was covered in a dull silver metal, fitting the body like skin. From the waist down it had a kangaroo or hare-like structure, dinner-plate shaped thighs and Z-legs with clawed feet. A curving glass stripe ran down each leg and Eliza could see whirring cogs, ornate, bronze clockwork and wires pulsing white.

Eliza thought the face and body quite ugly, once her fascination died down. But the hands. The hands spoke to her. She wanted to look at them closely and read that poetry. How beautiful they looked!

'Hello?' Eliza whispered.

The cyborg looked up and stared. Its fingers ran over the glass in the photo frame.

'I've brought you some clothes and food. I don't know if they'll help...but...I guess you're hiding?'

The cyborg smiled its human, female mouth and shook its head.

'You're not hiding, or the stuff won't help?'

The thing didn't answer. Eliza saw that its feet were shaking against the footboards.

'You can come indoors. I'll stay up late and leave the backdoor unlocked, if you decide you want to,' Eliza thought it best to leave it at that. There didn't seem any point in asking 'Who are you?' or 'What are you?' She put the backpack by the spades and closed the door, leaving it unlocked.

It didn't leave the shed.

Eliza waited three days but the thing didn't move. On the fourth day, she went back to check. The cyborg didn't seem to be moving at all. The photo-frame had dropped and cracked between its feet. Its hands hung by its sides and a cobweb hung between its thighs. The head rested back against the chair.

Moving inside, the smell of hot metal and chicken pellets filled Eliza's nose. She leaned over the cyborg, who failed to move or flinch like before. Eliza touched its forehead and poked it in the side. She slapped its thigh and tickled its neck, but nothing happened. The cyborg had died or broken down.

'You can't stay *here*, I need my shed,' Eliza muttered.

That night she went back out and managed to drag the heavy beast into her wheelbarrow. Then she wheeled it off to the studio-garage.

She had sold the car last year, as she lived near a well-stocked town and preferred public transport anyway. Then she'd got the decorators in. Wooden floor, insulated walls, good lighting and heating. Shelves sagged under the weight of boxes full of colours and clays. The walls were plastered with paintings, some hers, some prints of famous paintings. *The Girl with the Pearl Earring* peeped coyly from by the bins, as Eliza pulled the cyborg onto her large worktable.

Panting and cursing, Eliza sat down on a stool. The cyborg looked very pale...and *nibbled*. The ears had a curve of bite marks. One nostril had been eaten away.

A scratching, scurrying sound.

Eliza looked into the wheelbarrow to see two trapped mice.

'So you ate through a cyborg and now you're after my studio?' she hissed.

She caught the mice in a flowerpot, then tipped them into a Waitrose bag, tied it up tight and small, and dropped a brick on it. That dealt with, she turned back to the cyborg.

'So beautiful.' Eliza caressed the hands, running the fingers over her palm. The poems turned out to be *Howl* by Allen Ginsberg and *Mushrooms* by Sylvia Plath. Eliza had heard of them, they were part of that canon of philosophical, desperate nonsense keeping all the little poets at her former university busy.

'I wonder what happened to you,' Eliza mused, studying the cyborg's face. The hollow sockets looked more like a skull than ever and Eliza didn't like to stare into them for more than a few seconds.

'What am I going to do with you? Can't talk to the police, they'll take you away. No, no...it has got to be you and me. You have to stay.'

If she reported her find, the government wouldn't appreciate the hands like she did. They would take the cyborg apart and what, use the bits to fuel further ugly things? No! She would have to hide it somewhere. An idea popped into Eliza's head. She hurried back to the shed. The cyborg stayed on the artist's table, staring eyeless up at the lights.

Eliza came back with a saw. She gripped the cyborg's arm and began sawing just below the elbow. She would fix them to a mahogany square of wood and put them on the mantelpiece. If anyone asked, she'd say she got them from a little art shop in London. You could get everything in London.

She pulled out a large blanket box from the other side of the room and emptied it, shoved the box next to the table and pushed the now hand-less cyborg inside. The thing didn't quite fit. Eliza had to fold its half-arms and legs up at cruel angles, but finally she made it. She shoved the box under a wall shelf, found the old key for the box and locked the cyborg up.

A week later she hosted a dinner for some old work friends. They admired the bone-hands on the mantelpiece and asked her where she got them.

'Oh, a little place in London,' Eliza said. 'Southbank maybe.'

She had just finished handing out the wine, when Louise came back from the bathroom, looking quizzical.

'What have you got in that studio of yours, a wild animal?' she joked.

'What do you mean?' Eliza laughed.

'There's a lot of noise and banging.'

'I'll go and see. Help yourself to more wine everyone!' Eliza said.

One of the men in the party offered to help, but she waved him away.

Inside the garage, the blanket box had shuffled out from under the shelf and knocked over her easels. Eliza grabbed a brick from under her worktable.

Inside the box, the cyborg had been struggling to untwist its body. Eliza smiled wryly.

'Self-repairing are you?' she whispered, before bringing the brick hurtling down on the cyborg's head. One. Two. Three. Six. The cyborg's head caved in and the body went limp. The mouth hung open, flashing small teeth.

Eliza slammed the lid shut and went back to her dinner. 'Ugly thing.'

NOTES ON CONTRIBUTORS

All writers are winners of the annual Creative Writing Day anthology competition, organised by the Department of English and Creative Writing at the University of Roehampton. Unless stated otherwise, they are current or former students of the university and the degree BA Honours with Creative Writing (single or combined) as an award subject. Where applicable, the year of graduation is indicated in brackets.

MARITA ALGROY [2014] is a poet from Norway. She was awarded the Hopkins Poetry Prize in London (1st prize 2013 and 2014) and at the time of publication is working on a collection inspired by the film *La Jetée*. Each poem in the series *Screams & Silences* is written in response to a Munch painting and also shares its title.

RUDOLF AMMANN, PhD, is a humanities scholar, designer and chief artist at the Arkstack.co.uk media consultancy in North London. He has provided the templates, book cover and production workflow for Fincham Press since its launch.

NANOU BLAIR GOULD [2014] has, since graduating from Roehampton, taken her play *Fluff* to the Edinburgh Fringe Festival in Scotland. *Just Games* is her second short story to be published by Fincham Press. At the time of publication she is working on a screenplay and novel, *Turn Of The Weevil*. She became a vegetarian for ethical reasons but curiously, often kills animals in her stories.

FIONNUALA BLAND [2014] has published journalism in *The Forest Journal* newspaper and *La Dépêche du Midi*, a regional daily in France. Bland lives in Australia, where she is writing a travel blog. *Fire* is a piece of fantasy fiction set in seventeenth-century Scotland, during the witch trials.

NIKA COBBETT [2015] has worked for the university magazine *Fresh* as writer and editor. She writes in several forms, but always about people and the strange things they do, as a way to expose ugly truths. Her story *One of Those* intends to unsettle the reader.

ELLIOTT CODLING [2014] writes short fiction, poetry and novels. His writing usually explores and inverts social tropes. His short story *Running Away* aims to challenge images of childhood innocence with a story of loneliness and isolation.

DUSTIN FRAZIER WOOD, PhD, is an Anglo-Saxonist specialising in Old English literature and early modern medievalism. He recently completed his first book, *Anglo-Saxonism and the Idea of Englishness*. Frazier Wood is a research facilitator at the University of Roehampton, and a member of the Fincham Press editorial board.

ERICA GILLINGHAM (www.ericagillingham.com) is a PhD student with NCRCL at the University of Roehampton, researching lesbian love stories in young adult fiction. She received a BA in Literature (Creative Writing) and a second in Feminist Studies from UC Santa Cruz in 2007. Her poem revels in the intersections of sexuality and growing up with a local country radio station in the early 2000s. The title is influenced by Kim Addonizio's work, *This Poem Wants to Be a Rock and Roll Song So Bad* (2004).

SUSAN L GREENBERG, PhD, took up teaching and research after a long career as writer and editor for newspapers, magazines and the web. She is Senior Lecturer in the Department of English and Creative Writing at Roehampton, specialising in narrative nonfiction and publishing, and a founding member of the Fincham Press editorial board. Her latest book is *Editors talk about editing: insights for readers, writers and publishers* (Peter Lang, 2015).

KATHERINE GUTIERREZ cites literary influences that include the short stories of Haruki Murakami and Jorge Luis Borges. Her story *Angel Mountain* was inspired by an ancient Japanese haiku by Jito Tenno. This is her first submission to a competition.

MAJA HAGEN TORJUSSEN studied Communications, Media and Philosophy in Norway before coming to Roehampton. She has published nonfiction in the Norwegian web magazine *krs247.no*; poetry in the magazine *Bøygen*; and in 2015, a short story in the anthology *Fanzine*.

SILJE HEUM [2014] is a photographer and seasonal labourer whose work can be followed at medium.com/@heumsilje (words) and behance.net/heumsilje (pictures). When she wrote *Bring Your Own Sun*, she was spending a lot of time with young immigrants in London who had long stories they were reluctant to tell.

JAMIE HUBNER [2015] lives in Cumbria and writes short stories. He can be found on Twitter @Jhubs4. The work appearing here, his first published story, is inspired by an alarmingly regular tendency to recognise strangers in London, chase them, tap them on the shoulder, and then find he doesn't know them at all.

AUDREY JEAN [2015] is a visual artist and poet. Her visual compositions explore the relationship between poetry and the screen (outersoundspace.com). She is inspired by philosophy and physical cosmology. Her second poem to be published by Fincham Press, *721ˢᵗ day of falling,* records a star-ship captain's fragmented thoughts, revolving around his crew – and one crew member in particular.

HALEY JENKINS [2014] writes poetry and short stories and is working on her debut novel. Her work has been anthologised in *Painted, spoken, Open Pen* and *Tears in the Fence.* Jenkins works as a volunteer editor and production assistant at Veer Books, and with English PEN events at LonCon 3 and The London Book Fair. This is her second piece of work to be published by Fincham Press.

FRANCOISE MACALY [2014] is a writer and presenter for Midnight Madness, the biggest summer basketball competition in Britain. She writes its newsletter and hosts the basketball debate show, *About to Go In.* Macaly writes literary fiction and performance poetry. Her story, *Mother's Day,* is inspired by her grandmother and conveys the power of family and testimony.

EMILY PARSONS [2014] is a writer and youth worker from Tasmania. Her short stories have been published by Fincham Press and *Margins* online magazine. *Pinewood* explores the complexities of family: how we can turn our parents into saints or monsters, only to have those images shattered.

LEONE ROSS (leoneross.com) is a writer, teacher and editor and has been doing these things professionally for thirty years. Her novels, *All The Blood Is Red* (ARP) and *Orange Laughter* (Picador) were quietly but enthusiastically acclaimed in the late 1990s. She has spent the last decade publishing short stories, and writing a long – and funny – romance novel called *This One Sky Day.* The novel, along with a collection of stories, *Come Let Us Sing Anyway,* will be published in 2016. Ross is a Senior Lecturer in Creative

Writing at the University of Roehampton and member of the Fincham Press editorial board. She edited the press's first anthology, *The Trouble With Parallel Universes* (2014).

Jo Schinas [2014] writes prose fiction in a range of genres, including science fiction, particularly of the cyberpunk and biopunk variety. This is her second piece of work to be published by Fincham Press.

Victoria Simpkins [2015] writes fiction and plays, with a special interest in family structures and everyday relationships. Her stage play *Birthday* was inspired by people-watching in a pub on Christmas Eve.

Victoria Stevens [2015] is a fiction writer. Her short story *Star Theory* is inspired by a fascination with the constellations, and a hopeless romanticism. She was the winner of the Editor's Choice Award in the 2014 competition.

Charlotte Taverner [2014] writes web copy for an online retailer. When she's not reading, writing or blogging, she's exploring London. Taverner says that *A Trap For A Mole* is one of the most enjoyable writing experiences she's ever had.

Karoline Vembre [2014] is a writer from northern Norway. At the time of publication she is completing an MFA in Writing for Stage at the Central School of Speech and Drama, while working with Antistrophe Theatre Company. Her short story *Achromatic* is based on a news article about multiple suicides in one family and her poem *Movement* is inspired by Gertrude Stein's *Tender Buttons*.

Sean Wai Keung [2014] took an MA in Poetry at UEA Norwich, following graduation from Roehampton. He is deeply involved with UK performance poetry. His work (waikeung-poetry.wordpress.com) addresses the fears associated with memory, powerlessness and metaphor. The poems in this collection explore three very different forms of isolation and the inability to connect with the world outside the self. This is the second time Wai Keung's work has been published by Fincham Press.

CLEO WREFORD [2015] was the sort of child who could navigate a minefield with her nose in a book. She now writes fantasy and horror short stories and admires the work of Neil Gaiman and Mark Z. Danielewski. *Lunam* is a story about finding a true self, behind the veneer.